Index

tribal ceremonies, and possession, 81-3

tribal spirits, 115; possession by, 81, 82

tsambo (necklace), 139

tsangodzi tree, 172, 174

tsipa (goitre), 173

tsito (charcoal powder), 157

tsomo (axe), 80

tuberculosis, 139-40

underweight, medicine for, 73

unnatural actions, witches denoted by, 149*n*

urimbo tree, 174

uroyi (witchcraft), 46

vadzimu (ancestral spirits), 32, 33, 37

varoyi (witches), 43

vatete (aunt), 22*n*

village life, 17-23

Von Sicard, H., 76

weakness, marked, 166-7

Wedza reserve, 129

Whasai (a *nganga*), 127-8

White, C. M. N., 73

white witches, 31

wild pigs, ridden by witches, 44

Winda Pool, 61-2

witchcraft: cases of, in law courts, 144-51; charms against, 110-11

witches, 43-52; belief in sickness caused by, 24-5, 29, 30, 31, 134, 136, 140, 141, 142, 143, 170; difference between *nganga* and, 31; difference from *shave*, 41; good behaviour due to fear of, 51; inheritance of evil spirit from, 43; male, 45-6; naming of, 48-9, 144, 145, 146, 147, 149, 150, 151; protection against, 50-1; as scapegoats, 51; self-confessed, 47-8; witnesses important in naming of, 149*n*

wizi (breastplate), 80

women *nganga*: divination without *hakata*, 123, 128; qualifying methods, 123-4, 128-9

yakunama (divining throw), 78, 79

Yao chiefs, 26-7

zango charm, 111, 112, 173

zaru (divining throw), 78

zhambwa (powdered roots), 69

zinyakubaya roots, 172

Zulus, 45*n*

zumbani tree, 158*n*, 166

zuva root, 108

MICHAEL GELFAND

Witch Doctor

Traditional Medicine Man of Rhodesia

WITH A FOREWORD BY
SIR ROY WELENSKY
P.C., K.C.M.G.

FREDERICK A. PRAEGER, *Publishers*
NEW YORK · WASHINGTON

BOOKS THAT MATTER

Published in the United States of America in 1965
by Frederick A. Praeger, Inc., Publishers
111 Fourth Avenue, New York 3, N.Y.

© Michael Gelfand 1964

Library of Congress Catalog Card Number: 65-23415

FOR ANNE WITH LOVE

Printed in Great Britain

Foreword

When Dr Michael Gelfand arrived in Salisbury, aged twenty-six, he had already made something of a name for himself by earning at this early stage in his career the position of Consultant Physician. However, when he first arrived in the country the Southern Rhodesian Government had no particular use for his qualifications and found him a job as a radiologist for six months. From these humble beginnings has developed what I can only describe as a remarkable career.

Professor Michael Gelfand is the first Rhodesian to have been appointed to the Medical Faculty of the University College of Rhodesia and Nyasaland. It was an appointment that received general acclamation. As a man he has been twice honoured by his Sovereign for services to his fellow men. He received an O.B.E. and was subsequently raised to the rank of a Commander of the Most Excellent Order of the British Empire. Most of those who know of him and his work believe that in spite of his achievements he has, as yet, nowhere near approached the zenith of his career and they expect even greater things of him.

Professor Gelfand is one of the busiest physicians in this part of the world, and what has always appeared to me to be so remarkable about the man is, that he can give so generously of his time to the academic side of medicine and to helping in the essential task of placing on record the history of medicine in Central and other parts of Africa. His works in this field are already widely known.

In this, his latest book which deals with the Shona

doctor, Professor Gelfand has tackled a task that badly needed attention. He has tried, and I think succeeded, in removing the preconceived and erroneous fallacy that is so widely held in the outside world that the African witch-doctor is of necessity evil.

Professor Gelfand writes in language that ordinary men and women, who have no medical knowledge, can understand. He gives a picture of the Shona customs, customs which the vast majority of Europeans do not know of and, most important of all, he places the witch-doctor in his correct context. Reading this book, one becomes aware that amongst other things the Shona doctor is often a herbalist of quality, that he practises preventive medicine and, last but not least, that he is a respected member of his community and leads the same life as the other men of his village when not engaged in his medical practice.

It may come as a surprise to many that the Shona doctor is given no special status in the village and is only accorded the respect that is associated with his medical ability.

I believe we ought to be grateful to Professor Gelfand for destroying the Hollywood version of the witch-doctor that dominates the thinking on this subject of the vast majority of ill-informed people.

It is interesting to observe that medical men have played a very important part in Africa's destiny, from the witch-doctors who advised Shaka, Dingaan and Lobengula, acted as their wise men and treated their physical complaints, to doctors of our own civilization, men cast in the mould of Albert Schweitzer, David Livingstone and the man who did so much for the advance of African health in this part of the world—Godfrey Huggins, now Lord Malvern.

To this list I would add without hesitation the name of Professor Gelfand. He is of that company.

Salisbury,
Southern Rhodesia   *Roy Welensky*

Contents

Contents

Illustrations

Illustrations

Preface

I was born and brought up in the Cape and have always had a deep attachment for the African. As a small child, I used to watch the men who collected in the evenings in small groups, sitting and talking with their short pipes in their mouths and their blankets drawn over their shoulders, and as soon as I was old enough I used to go and sit with them.

I first came into contact with the African as a patient when I came to Rhodesia twenty-five years ago. I was appointed Government Medical Officer in Salisbury after qualifying in South Africa and I soon became so absorbed in the medical problems of the Africans that I devoted more and more of my time to them. As I got to know my patients better, I realized that most of them were also consulting their own doctors and that I was only a small cog in a wheel about which I knew very little. And so I was drawn, very willingly, to a study of Shona medicine, a study which led inevitably to the rituals, religion and customs of the Shona people.

Mashonaland covers the greater portion of Southern Rhodesia. The Shona name for their 'doctors' is *nganga*. Unfortunately, the European has never found an adequate translation for this word and has loosely described unqualified African doctors all over the continent as 'witch doctors'. Many authorities, and Africans themselves, object to this term as it implies that the *nganga* is a witch, when one of his functions is to eradicate witchcraft. But this is only one of his duties. The Shona word *nganga* is broad enough to include his other functions and loose enough to describe the different kinds of doctor: herbalist, diviner, specialist. To replace 'witch doctor' by 'herbalist' or 'diviner' lands us in another difficulty as some *nganga* are both diviners and herbalists. And as 'medicine man', the usual European alternative to 'witch doctor', is also misleading I propose to call the Shona doctor in this book by his Shona name—*nganga*.

At first I began to accumulate information about the *nganga* by questioning my African medical orderlies. But in 1943 I had the good fortune to meet an elderly missionary, Father Burbridge, who was interested in a book I had just published.[1] He had spent most of his life amongst the Shona tribes and was particularly interested in the *nganga* and their practices. Until his death three years later, we met and talked regularly, and from his vast experience he taught me many things about the Mashona. With increasing confidence I began to contact the *nganga* and discovered for myself how closely they were associated with the spiritual as well as the physical lives of their patients. I never had any difficulty in gaining the confidence and sympathy of these men and should like to thank them here for their ready co-operation, without which this book could never have been written.

I shall always remember with gratitude the assistance I received throughout my field studies from my African orderlies, Mr Shorgai Matonhodze and Mr Stanley Masuko. Father Hannan, s.j., of Kutama Mission was my constant guide and critic in this research and I am indebted in the manuscript stage to Dr Beth Granger, Dr H. Wild, Mrs G. L. Barlow, Dr V. N. Barlow, Mr A. H. S. Fletcher, and to my wife.

I am grateful, too, to Dr I. M. Lewis of Glasgow University, who, when lecturing on social anthropology at the

[1] *The Sick African*

Preface

University College of Rhodesia and Nyasaland, encouraged me to collect details of the visits made by my patients to their *nganga*.

University College of Rhodesia and Nyasaland
Salisbury
Southern Rhodesia

PART I

The Nganga

CHAPTER I

The nganga in ordinary life

Before going into the *nganga*'s medical activities, it is useful to know how he and his patients live. Shona community life is based on the village, and the peculiar characteristic of a Shona village is that almost all the inhabitants are related to each other; it is, in fact, an extension of the family unit.

A village, known as a *musha*, can be any size. In its smallest form it consists of one family: a husband, his wife or wives, his children and, if they are alive, his parents. It may consist of several, or a great number of families, all related to each other on the paternal side and adding up to a population of one hundred or more. As each family has several huts and owns a plot of land, a large village may cover an area of over a mile.

Every *musha*, large or small, is built along the same lines. Each family group has one main hut called the *imba*. This is where the husband and wife sleep, where the wife cooks and where the whole family lives in the daytime. When their children are small they sleep there too, but at the age of seven or eight they leave the *imba*, the boys to share a hut called the *gota* and the girls to another called the *nhanga*. The husband's parents live and sleep in their own *imba* and usually one of their granddaughters moves in with them instead of going to the girls' *nhanga*. She helps them with their daily chores and lives with them until she is grown up.

The central feature of an *imba* is the fireplace where the

food is prepared and cooked. The wife and her daughters eat here, but the husband and his sons have their meals at a special place in the village called the *dare*. This is a small clearing, usually just beyond the periphery of huts; it is used not only for meals but as a meeting place for the men when important village matters are discussed. The men sit on stones or logs round the fire in the middle of the clearing. No woman is allowed to sit in the *dare*, her presence there is confined to bringing her husband his food. She kneels to hand it to him and then returns to the *imba* where the women of the family congregate to eat their meal sitting on the floor of the hut.

The family's plot of land, called a *munda*, or garden, is about one acre in size, sometimes a little more. Husband and wife till this plot together and each owns a portion of it. They plant a mixture of maize, finger-millet, bulrush millet, Kaffircorn, beans, monkey nuts (planted only by the women), rice, pumpkins and sweet potatoes. At special times of the year, when planting, weeding or reaping have to be done, the husband notifies his relatives and his friends in neighbouring villages and everyone comes to help. This is a happy and festive time and after the work is done the owner rewards the helpers by giving them beer brewed by his wife.[1]

Each family has one or more granaries and the women help themselves to the grain or anything they need for cooking. They stamp the grain in a mortar, grind it to meal on a stone and then cook it into a thick porridge known as *sadza*. This is the staple diet of Mashonaland and it is always served with a relish of some kind, cooked vegetable leaves and peanut butter, or, very occasionally, a meat stew.

Just outside the village is the communal cattle kraal, or *danga*, a circular area enclosed by a fence of wooden poles.

---

[1] This beer party is called a *hoka*. Beer is always made by the women in Mashonaland; its preparation takes ten days and finger-millet is the usual basis.

Most families own several head of cattle, it is the most
tangible status of wealth and is still used as a basis for cal-
culating the *lobolo*,[1] or bride money.

The affairs of the *musha* are run by the elders of the village
—the grandfathers and older men. A *musha* of any size will
also have its headman, called a *sabuku*, who is appointed by
the local chief. When problems or disputes cannot be
settled by the *sabuku* and the elders, the *sabuku* takes them
before the chief.

There is no paramount chief in Mashonaland, the country
is split into many districts each ruled by its own hereditary
chief who may have a varying number of sub-chiefs under
him. When the headman of a village brings him an unresolved dispute, he will either pronounce judgment himself
at his own court (with the help of his several councillors or
advisers, who are usually his relatives), or if he considers the
matter outside his jurisdiction[2] he will refer it to the local
District Commissioner, an official of the Administration.

When attending a social or religious function in a *musha*,
I am always struck by the correctness of Shona behaviour;
it is apparently based on a very strict code of etiquette which
is understood by everyone present. In fact, the precedence
and duties of each individual are so clearly defined that
there is never any discussion about who offers the prayers at
a religious gathering, who speaks on an important occasion,
who hands out the beer or receives the first cup at a beer

[1] *Lobolo* is the sum paid to the girl's father by the father of the boy who
is going to marry her. No marriage is legal in African law without this
payment; it not only compensates the father for the loss of his daughter
but through it he renounces any claim on her children who, in the
event of her death, are the 'property' of her husband. If a wife leaves
her husband for no good reason he can re-claim the *lobolo* from his
father-in-law.
[2] Family quarrels, complaints against the headman, the custody of
children and marital disputes are all matters which are judged according
to African law and customs, and therefore come under the jurisdiction
of the Chief; all criminal offences such as murder, theft and arson must
be referred to the District Commissioner.

party. Precedence is, of course, related to age but the formality of Shona manners is not confined to this type of occasion or to respect for the old; it extends to the everyday life of the family and to the greeting of strangers and visitors.

This greeting is performed in a slow and deliberate manner by both parties. Let us imagine that the men are sitting in their *dare*, the stranger approaches the circle, he sits down quietly, claps his hands two or three times and then listens while the men continue their talk. At a suitable break in the discussion he claps his hands again, and is answered by a similar clap from the most senior of the villagers. This means that he is welcome and may now give the reasons for his visit. When he leaves, and if his visit has lasted several days, he is not bidden farewell at the entrance of the village, but is accompanied for half a mile or more before the villagers take leave of him—a courtesy which implies an interest in the visitor up to the last moment of his visit, pleasure in his company, and a reluctance to part with him.

Friends and relations greet each other according to age and seniority. The younger must be the first to do so and to enquire how the older one is, except in the case of a son-in-law who must always be the first to make these advances when he meets any of his father-in-law's family, whatever their age. Hands are not shaken unless the occasion lends itself; the usual greeting is made by clapping hands, men clap with their palms and fingers extended, women with the palms of their hands at a right angle. If a woman meets an older person on her path she claps her hands in the usual way and at the same time flexes both knees to one side to an angle of 20°. She does this obeisance also when she hands over an article to her husband or any senior man of the family. A man will make this sideways curtsey only when he meets his grandmother or another old and respected woman. When greeting an important person, such as a chief, the men sit on the ground and clap their hands twice when the chief enters their circle. After a silence of ten seconds, they clap their hands again in unison, very fast, and keep up this rhythmic clapping for roughly one minute.

Shona eating habits too are regulated by a special code of behaviour. For instance, no man at the *dare* starts to eat before his elders, he must chew a morsel of food very slowly so that he does not finish before the older men; nor, of course, must he ever rise and walk off while others are still eating. I have often noticed that if an African is given some food, he does not eat it alone, however hungry he may be, but shares it with whomever he happens to be with. The Shona child is brought up on the principle that food must be shared, it is symptomatic of the closeness of Shona family life because though the men and women eat separately they never eat alone and very often their *sadza* is shared from a common plate.

Correct behaviour, good manners and discipline are an inescapable part of a Shona child's upbringing. The whole family takes a hand in his education, the parents teach obedience and administer punishment when necessary, the grandparents tell him how he should behave towards his seniors and towards visitors and strangers, while his aunts—on the paternal side—teach him the correct relationship towards the opposite sex. This family education continues until marriage and is seldom rebelled against. The more one studies traditional Shona manners, and the way in which these are instilled in their children, the more one realizes that their basis is that of all good manners—a consideration for the feelings of others.

How to receive and how to return a present are also arts practised by the Shona. However small the gift, the person receiving it first claps his hands quickly once or twice and then extends them palms upwards, little fingers touching, towards the giver, a gesture which combines humility with the implication that the present is so large and so precious that the recipient needs both hands to hold it.[1] The Shona always returns a present—not with something of the same value—but with a token gift. He applies this principle of giving something in return to anyone who does him a service, like helping him with his crops; and in their turn each guest at a beer party brings a small present for the host.

In settling quarrels the Mashona have learnt the wisdom of the 'indirect approach' which allows for negotiation through a third person and encourages the antagonists to keep apart at a time when their tempers are frayed and a good human relationship might be lost. In minor family quarrels it is the father's eldest sister and her family who try and settle the dispute. The important factor is the delay which reduces the emotional content of the argument and encourages a more equitable solution.

The indirect approach is particularly well illustrated in the preliminaries leading to marriage—a situation full of potential high feeling between parents and children as well as between the two families. A son, having made up his mind whom he wants to marry, goes to his father's eldest sister[2] and tells her everything he knows about the girl and her family. She then discusses the marriage with her brother; if his reaction is not favourable, she will tell the boy to wait for a while in the hope that the father may change his mind. But if the marriage is considered suitable the father talks to his son and puts the negotiations with the girl's family into the hands of a *munyai*, or go-between. Thanks to the *munyai* the two families avoid meeting each other until all the arrangements are made, including the delicate one of settling the *lobolo*. One hears so often that the African's progress started with the arrival of the European that one is apt to forget the civilized form of human relationships and behaviour that he had evolved for himself.

To return to the *nganga*, when he is not engaged in his

[1] This gesture of receiving is known as *kugamuchira* or *kutambira*.
[2] *Vatete*.

medical practice he leads exactly the same life as the other men of his village. He cultivates his land, looks after his cattle, repairs his huts, makes blankets or other equipment needed by his family. And the same applies to a woman *nganga*, who busies herself with the tasks expected of every Shona woman: the preparation and cooking of food, the collecting of water and firewood, the making of pots, the care of the land, the smearing of the hut floors with cow-dung and last, but not least, with the preparation of beer. The amount the *nganga* does in his village depends, of course, on the demands of his patients, but on the average he has a fair amount of spare time.

People in each region know by word of mouth where the *nganga* lives, no distinguishing feature singles out his hut from the others in the village. It is difficult to give a very accurate estimate of the number of *nganga* per ratio of population in one particular district, but a fair guess would be one to every 800 to 1,000 persons. In villages which boast of a resident chief, one or more *nganga* may live close to each other in order to attend the chief and his family. There is no apparent shortage of *nganga*, I have never heard an African complain that he could not find one when he was needed. The only complaint I have heard, and this was only made to me once, was from the relative of a patient who had difficulty in persuading a particular *nganga* to leave his hut at night to visit the patient's home. There is, of course, a greater concentration of *nganga* in the towns, where there is a great demand for their remedies and where most of them practise as herbalists.

The *nganga* is given no special status in his village, his chances of being appointed headman are the same as anyone else's. The measure of respect and regard in which he is held by the rest of the village depends entirely on his professional skill and ability.

CHAPTER 2

The nganga: magician or spiritualist?

It is strange that the *nganga* who figures so prominently in every description of the indigenous people of Africa, who, furthermore, is one of the few Africans to have achieved professional status in his natural environment, should be misrepresented so often. This is the case even inside Africa, while to those outside the country his name is synonymous with a strange, frightening, unscrupulous and dangerous person whose magic is feared by all. The real figure is neither as strange nor as romantic as the mythical one. In his own community, the *nganga* is esteemed and respected and lives, as we have seen, the same kind of life as any other Shona man. His patients look on him as someone capable of curing them when they are sick, of advising them in misfortune and in the many problems which crop up in ordinary life.

How does the *nganga* function as a doctor? When a patient consults him for sickness, his first action is to diagnose the cause of the illness, not in physical terms, but in spiritual ones, because Africans believe that sickness is caused either by the activity of spirits (usually those of their dead relatives) or by men and women who are evil and desire to harm others. These are the dreaded witches and they are more often women than men.

Very briefly, the *nganga*'s treatment consists in finding out whether a witch or a spirit has caused the illness, in advising his patients on the procedure necessary to propitiate whichever is the cause, and in prescribing the right herbal remedy to cure the physical damage already sustained by the patient. The *nganga*'s medical practice is therefore part spiritual and part homeopathic.

The next question is, what is the basis of the *nganga*'s skill and ability? When I first became interested in the *nganga*'s technique I approached him with the idea that he was a magician and that much of what he practised was based on symbolism, or what anthropologists call sympathetic and contagious magic. My observations of what the *nganga* did appeared at first to bear out this conception. For instance, to give a man strength the *nganga* prescribed the heart of a lion, for security and solidarity—a portion of the body of a tortoise, for swiftness—the sinew of a hare, and for a woman wanting to increase her flow of milk—the milky sap of a certain tree. Like was evidently expected to produce like. The contagious aspect of this magic consists in transferring by touch a certain quality from a particular site to another. But I discovered that physical contact was not always necessary, sometimes the *nganga* took a property from its source and transferred it to a person simply by mentioning his name. All this seemed to confirm my belief that the *nganga* was considered by his patients to have an inherent gift with which he could manipulate circumstances to bring about a desired effect and that the basis of his practice was magic.

But when I asked the Mashona how they accounted for the cures attributed to the *nganga*, I found that they associated them with the potency of the medicines he prescribed and believed that it was the *nganga*'s knowledge of the right medicine, and not any special quality inherent in him, that mattered. Medicines are believed not only to cure disease, but in some cases to confer positive virtues on those who take them. It is the African's faith in the potency of the medicine that makes it possible for him to assume, by an extension of thought, that the medicine can operate from a distance and without physical contact.

This faith in medicine and the importance of possessing the right one is illustrated by the following myth which is believed to be true by the majority of Mashona. In the Zimbabwe area, about 200 miles south of Salisbury, there once lived a man named Nyanhehwe. He was not a *nganga*, but the founder of a large Shona tribe, and, according to the legend, a famous rain-maker. He had acquired his great fame and power because of the special 'medicine' he possessed which invested him with superhuman qualities whenever he took it. After a time he decided to move 400 miles northwards to Makorekore country. Wherever he went, thanks to his magical medicines, he instilled fear and men fled from him; finally, when he decided to settle in a village in this new land, the headman disappeared and Nyanhehwe married his six wives. One year no rain fell in his area, although not far away rain was plentiful in a region where Dzivaguru, another powerful rain-maker, held sway. Nyanhehwe was so annoyed at seeing his reputation as a rain-maker jeopardized that he decided to visit Dzivaguru. When he reached his rival's district, he could not see the land ahead because of the haze from the flood waters. He sat down and ate some of his special medicine, and immediately the haze disappeared. Able now to see the land in front of him, he chased Dzivaguru away to the top of a nearby mountain. Today the spirit of Nyanhehwe is believed to rule over and protect this tribe and they pray to him as a rain-maker in time of drought.

A true incident, also showing the African's belief in the powers of medicine, occurred about seventy years ago during the wars in Nyasaland. The Yao chiefs, who were fighting the British to preserve their slave trade, employed *nganga* to provide them with medicines to help them in battle. One chief was convinced by his *nganga* that if he took the medicine he gave him it would render him invisible and thus enable him to move unseen amongst the European forces and kill at close range. The medicine failed, but not the chief's faith in it, and the British soldiers were amazed to see him rushing unconcernedly into the thickest fire where he soon lost his life.

The *nganga* himself denies that knowing the right medicines or divining the cause of illness is a personal talent. He claims that his ability and skill are due to a special spiritual endowment. In many cases this endowment comes to him from the spirit of a dead relative who was a *nganga* during life and who wished for his skill and experience to continue after death through a living member of his family. The *nganga* therefore claims that it is not he, the corporeal *nganga*, who diagnoses the cause of illness or prescribes the right treatment, but the healing spirit of his relative who enters him (literally taking possession of him) when he divines and often too when he is asleep, revealing to him in dreams the remedy he should prescribe and where he should look for a particular herb.

Falling into a state af possession by their spirits is a characteristic of most *nganga*. It can best be described as a trance, although it is difficult to exclude hysteria or hypnosis as an explanation. While they are in this state, the mediums are believed to be 'out of this world' although they talk, move about, and answer questions. At tribal ceremonies, the entry of tribal spirits into their hosts, or mediums, is a complicated affair accompanied by prolonged dancing and music, and it may take several hours for the medium to pass into a state of possession. But the *nganga* becomes possessed by his healing spirit very easily, sometimes simply by clapping his hands. In the same way, when the spirit departs he seems to return from his trance without much ado or outward sign. But this, I have been told by the *nganga*, is because the longer a person has been a medium, and presumably the more experienced he is, the less effort is required for him to enter or withdraw from a trance.

Dealing with the cause and effects of illness is only part of the *nganga*'s duties. He is a diviner of the causes of death who identifies his clients before they have spoken to him, telling them why they have come and who has died. He is expected to act as a prophet, warning his clients of future misfortune, foretelling the outcome of a contemplated venture, and answering any questions put to him. He also uses his gift of divination in instances affecting the good of the community; for example, to discover the loss of an article or animal and the identity of the thief. He is nearly always successful in this work, and one wonders how he achieves his results. Are they due, perhaps, to an efficient information system and to the fact that the *nganga* is probably the most intelligent person in his community and also no mean psychologist?

The whole atmosphere surrounding the *nganga*, then, is one of wonder which derives from his spiritual powers and the degree of intimacy he is believed to enjoy with the world of spirits through the agency of his healing spirit. The *nganga* believes that if for some reason his healing spirit were to forsake him, he would lose his powers of vision and clair-voyance and he would be unable to function as a *nganga* until he had propitiated the spirit and persuaded it to return to him. On his own evidence, therefore, the *nganga* appears to be more of a spiritualist than a magician.

In so vast a continent as Africa, there are naturally many differences among the *nganga* of different areas. But just as there is a similarity in the practice of Western medicine, so there is a similarity in the way the *nganga* of Kenya, the Congo, and Mashonaland deal with sickness. All start from the same premise that the cause is spiritual rather than physical, though treatment of the physical symptoms may differ widely from tribe to tribe. Most *nganga* believe that nature provides cures and remedies for most types of illness, either in the form of plants and trees, or in natural matter such as the excreta of certain animals and birds, or in particular parts of their bodies.

Although I personally have never met a 'bad' *nganga* who practised evil, or cast spells upon others, I have frequently been told by the Mashona that they exist. They are the sorcerers, or black magicians, mentioned by observers in other parts of Africa. The Mashona regard these *nganga* as doctors who use their healing spirits to achieve their own ends, thus misusing the spiritual force. By surreptitiously procuring a piece of the victim's clothing, nail parings, hair-clippings, or excreta, and casting a spell or 'doctoring' this material, the 'bad' *nganga* is able to harm the victim whose soul is believed to be in these materials.[1] A man is bewitched if an enchanted object (for instance, a sharp piece of bone doctored with a special medicine) is planted along his path, the evil being transferred to him as he walks over it. As in the practice of 'good' medicine, a spell may operate through an extension of contact, a victim may be struck down many miles away from the actual site of the rite merely by the utterance of his name. Whether the *nganga* casts this spell himself or sells the doctored material to someone else to use, he is considered a witch and so is the person who has bought it. The Mashona describe this type of witch as one who practises in the day, in contradistinction to the classical witch, a female, who carries out her malpractices at night.

Certain authorities on Africa believe that the *nganga*'s skill is not spiritual but magical. The well-known anthropologist, Professor Evans-Pritchard of Oxford University, defines this magic as a 'technique that is supposed to achieve its purpose by the use of medicines. The operation of these medicines is a magic rite and is usually accompanied by a spell'. He describes three types of 'medicine men' among the Azande in the Sudan. The magician: 'any person who possesses medicines and uses them in magical rites'; the sorcerer: 'anyone who possesses bad medicines and uses them in rites of sorcery'; and the witch doctor, called *abinza* in the Sudan,

---

[1] Incidentally, this belief ensures a high standard of tidiness and hygiene because excreta, old clothes and rubbish etc., are always hidden in a concealed part of the bush outside the village to minimize the danger of its being doctored by a witch.

who is 'the diviner who diagnoses and combats witchcraft in virtue of medicines which he has eaten, by certain dances and by leechcraft'. [1]

My experience with the Shona *nganga* differs in several respects from Evans-Pritchard's description of the Sudan *abinza*. Firstly, the Shona *nganga* seldom operates by taking medicine himself. Secondly, both he and his patients believe that his ability stems from his spiritual endowment. Remove the supernatural influence, and the *nganga* becomes the same as any other person. His patients believe in the potency of his medicines because they believe in their supernatural source, having been revealed to the *nganga* by his healing spirit.

Other authorities, such as M. J. Field, [2] who carried out her researches among the Ga people in West Africa, believe that in order for his medicines to be effective, the *nganga* must carry out a prescribed ritual—one of the essentials for a magician. It is held that magicians work in this manner while a witch operates on a spiritually higher plane and without palpable apparatus. Again, this is not borne out by my experience with the Mashona. Certainly they believe that the witch, like the *nganga*, is spiritually endowed with a spirit which is evil and operates against the interests of mankind, but the Shona witch does, in fact, use palpable apparatus, such as 'doctored' material or food to make her witchcraft effective. As to the prescribed rituals of the *nganga*, I believe these are intended more to please the healing spirit than as a magical rite, in the same way that a member of a religious order wears special apparel as a sign of his order and carries out the precise ritual of a religious service to please God and impress on his congregation the solemnity of the occasion.

And now what conclusion can we come to about the

---

[1] E. Evans-Pritchard, *Witchcraft, Oracles and Magic among the Azande*, Clarendon Press, pp. 109–11.
[2] M. J. Field, *Religion and Medicine of the Ga People*, Oxford University Press.

nganga as a spiritualist or a magician? The truth of the matter seems to lie in what is meant by the term 'magic'. I was rather surprised to learn that there is no Shona word for magic in a language which is rich and descriptive. According to the Oxford dictionary, magic is 'the pretended art of influencing the course of events by compelling the agency of spiritual beings, or by bringing into operation some occult controlling principle of nature'. This definition is, I think, more in keeping with the African's idea of magic as applied to the *nganga* than the meaning sometimes given to it by anthropologists.

Basically the only difference between the witch and the *nganga* is the eternal one between good and evil. The witch manipulates the occult forces through her evil spirit to the detriment of man, while the *nganga* manipulates them for the good through his healing spirit.

In Europe, where once the same situation existed, men and women who practised witchcraft in order to cure disease were known as 'white witches' and their remedies were much sought after. In this sense one might call the *nganga* a 'white magician'.

The *nganga*'s approach to sickness is not on rational lines, he is no scientist, but one is obliged to admit that he practises an art with superb skill. Medicine in the Western world was once both a science and an art, but as the scientific approach looms more and more to the fore, there is less emphasis on the art. The *nganga* is the artist *par excellence*. He uses every means—dress, amulets, beads, incantations and rituals—to impress his clients and win their confidence, and in this respect he is an unqualified success.

CHAPTER 3

Ancestral, or guardian, spirits

Before saying more about the *nganga* it is useful to know something about the beliefs of his patients and their reasons for consulting him.

Believing that sickness, misfortune and death are accounted for by the activity of spirits, Africans argue, as Europeans might, that once the cause of an illness is diagnosed, the cure becomes relatively easy. In their case, either the offended spirit must be propitiated or the evil removed (if a witch is the cause) and recovery will follow. As far as the Mashona are concerned, there are four spiritual causes of disease; some are more important than others, but each has its own significance which must be taken into account. They are: the spirits of their ancestors—*vadzimu*; the alien and patronal spirits—*mashave*; the aggrieved spirit—*ngozi*; and the evil spirit of the witch—*muroyi*.

The Mashona believe that after death the spirit of a person enters into a spiritual world in which it lives a life still closely bound to the earth. The spirits of their dead relations hover around their villages, in the house-tops, in the forests, on the hills, in the trees, in pools or in the depths of the earth. In their spirit world they eat, drink and take snuff, are in harmony with each other, with other groups of spirits and with their living relations. Unlike Greek and Roman deities, they do not argue or take part in battle, for individual rivalries no longer exist among them.

Only the spirit of a married person is important for a spirit can only look after and guard its blood relations—protecting the living members from disease and disaster, and ensuring that their children's children continue to prosper in the village. If the family remember their dead they will be safe and happy and, most important of all, their homes will be guarded against the entry of a witch. A child as he grows is trained in the worship of his family spirits and is also instructed to show reverence to his living relations. He must show respect not only to his father and mother but to their parents and indeed, to all other members of the family. Amongst the Shona people and, in my experience, with all African peoples, discipline, good manners and respect count very high among the virtues. Men and women have their proper respective places in society, and each relation has a defined position in the family. As the father and mother grow older, respect and regard for them increase so that by the time they become grandparents, they receive every consideration. We have seen how they are given a hut of their own to live in and how a grandchild, or sometimes even two, is delegated to fetch and carry for them, and does any work they cannot manage themselves on their piece of land. They are consulted on family procedure, are called upon to settle quarrels and differences between younger members of the family and are respected and listened to by everyone in virtue of their position as elders of the village. They teach the children good manners and the grandmother may even instruct the girls on sexual matters. As the elderly grow still older, they seem to pass almost imperceptibly into the other world.

The link between living and dead is very close; much closer, I believe, than in European society. The Mashona love and revere their dead and, in time of need, turn to their *vadzimu* in the same way as the Christian turns to God. The actions of the traditionally raised Africans are dominated by this combination of love and fear of the spirits, for they believe that their guardian spirits can punish as well as protect, and will bring sickness and even death to those who disregard or forget them. Their needs and wishes must not be questioned and sometimes, even if the family has broken no rules and is leading a good life, one of the spirits may bring sickness to a member merely because it wants to be remembered.

Guardian spirits are easily upset if religious ritual is omitted; for instance, a burial at which the prescribed ritual had been forgotten would certainly arouse the wrath of the spirit and the guilty family would be punished, though the offended spirit might not show its annoyance until months or even years after the event.

It is impossible to foretell how the guardian spirit will strike. It may cause an illness severe enough for the family to consult a *nganga* and more often than not the victim is an infant or child. Perhaps this is because the child is the Mashona's greatest treasure and if he becomes ill his parents will be so upset that they will be only too anxious to propitiate the aggrieved spirit.

The spirits of both parents and grandparents are able to inflict an illness, but since the spirit which requires to be revered and remembered above all others is that of the grandfather, or *sekuru*, this is the spirit that is most often held responsible for sickness. One way of honouring the spirit of the grandfather is to name a bull after him. This bull is worked with the other domestic animals, but it may not be sold or killed unless the *sekuru* asks for it—through the *nganga*—it will then be sacrificed at a special ceremony, after which the head of the family prays to the *sekuru*, informing him that his wishes have been carried out and asking him to keep the family well and free from all trouble.

A grandmother's spirit, too, can be annoyed and inflict most ferocious punishments. If, for instance, during life, she was not presented with a cow in honour of her own mother by one of her sons-in-law, she is almost certain to remember the slight after death.

The spirits of a dead father or mother are not involved anything like as frequently as the spirits of the grandparents. In some tribes, for example the Makorekore, only the spirits of the grandparents are important; for they believe that no man or woman can receive a proper place in the next world unless he or she has a grandchild, which may explain the great desire of the African to bear children.

The spirit of a grandfather usually causes a grandson to become ill, while a grandmother is more likely to be responsible for the sickness of a granddaughter.

Admiration for Western civilization and its achievements does not deflect Africans from their attachment to these guardian spirits and many who profess Christianity would hesitate to deny their conviction that the spirits of their departed ancestors wield great influence over their lives. On the other hand, they are sensitive about these beliefs because they are afraid that most Europeans will laugh at them and look down on their ritual practices. As a result, few Europeans are well informed about these interesting religious rites.

The Africans are easily upset by any suggestion that their parents were primitive or uneducated; one of the features of their religion is that, even if their parents did not lead very admirable lives, they are still remembered kindly and reverently by their children. For now that they are dead they will have already paid the price for any bad thing they did during their lives because punishment for a wicked life, with certain exceptions which we shall touch upon later, is restricted to this world, therefore after death there are no recriminations and the spirit lives in company with and on an equal basis with other spirits.

How do the guardian spirits view the behaviour of their children on earth? It is not easy to be certain how much these spirits are regarded as influencing the ordinary daily behaviour of the Shona, but it is believed that the guardian spirits are not only upset if a religious practice or customs i broken or neglected, but also if a son is cruel or unkind to his parents or speaks harshly to them.

If a woman is ill-treated by one of her children, after her death her spirit will cause him or one of his children to become ill, usually the victim develops mental confusion. Then the patient will consult a *nganga* who, discovering the cause of the spirit's grievance, will tell him how it must be appeased. He may have to take part in a special ceremony known as *kutiza botso:* dressing himself in rags, he must walk for miles, from village to village, begging for grain. Each time he comes to a village he picks up a small piece of earth and blows the sand out of his hand saying, 'Grandmother, you left your snuff box'. This is an admission that he wronged her when she was alive. After he has visited all the neighbouring villages, he returns home and has some beer brewed with the grain he has collected and when it is ready, a ceremony is held in honour of the spirit who will usually be propitiated and cease to cause illness in the family.

Although the guardian spirits do not approve of bad deeds, such as stealing and adultery, they seem as a rule to leave the punishment of such crimes to the law of the land or to the *nganga*, who has special powers for discovering such wrongdoers; but occasionally a grandfather's spirit may notice that one of his family is committing an anti-social act and it will then speak to the villagers through the medium of a son or grandson and warn them that one of their flesh and blood is breaking the law, and that unless he stops he will be discovered and punished.

An example of an African's close relationship with his guardian spirits is his silent prayer of thanks to them every time he receives any kind of gift. Also whenever he undertakes an important venture he will pray to the spirit of his grandfather to ask for its support so that the outcome will be successful. In the same way, if, for instance, a man finds that his business is not prospering as it did in the past, he visits the *nganga* who may tell him that his misfortune is due to the fact that on some previous occasion he has neglected one of his guardian spirits. The remedy is an easy one for if he makes the desired and necessary amends the business will soon become successful again.

Guardian spirits exercise a restraining influence which affects the daily behaviour of the Shona. Tradition is treasured by the conservative tribal African and for this reason 'progressive' opinions and new ideas often encounter great opposition among the older Africans. The *vadzimu*, they hold, do not encourage their earthly children to strive for progress, and consequently they feel that what was good enough for their grandfathers and grandmothers is good enough for them. The key word to African philosophy is ' normality '.

The prayer of a Shona to his *vadzimu* is not a daily prayer, but is said only when there is need for it. Ordinarily it is the male head of the family who offers the prayer on behalf of one of its members, and a woman would entrust this duty not to her husband, but to the senior male member of her own family. This refers to formal prayers, but of course, silent thanks or sudden pleas for help can be said by anyone in times of joy or of need.

Formal prayers to ancestral spirits are usually said in front of the *rukuva*—the shelf upon which the cooking-pots are stacked. The family gather before it and the head of the family, wearing a black prayer-shawl, similar to the white one worn in a synagogue, kneels to pray.

An angered ancestral spirit may demand propitiation in the form of beer, or it may insist that the animal named after it be killed. In these days, however, the spirits' requirements have become so up to date that it is not unusual for the *nganga* to inform his client that the spirit would like a blanket, a coat or a dress. [1]

Owing to the rapid social, economic and political changes that are taking place in Africa today, the practices of genuine spirit-ritual are dying out but the underlying belief remains strong, and even if fewer families keep a bull in honour of the grandfather's spirit, a cow or its equivalent must still be given to a bride's mother by the bridegroom. Possibly the reason for continuing this practice is the fear that, after death, she might cause sterility in her daughter or grand-daughters.

Quite a lot of Africans who have become Christians consult both Church and the *nganga* when they are in trouble for they do not see any contradiction in accepting Christianity and believing in the power of the spirit elders. A *nganga* with whom I discussed this point reminded me that in Church the dead are remembered in special prayers while another African suggested that when Europeans visit cemeteries and place flowers on the graves of their relations, they are, in fact, practising a form of *mudzimu*[2] worship and he added: 'Were not prayers said at the graves?' Thus an African often feels that he can be a Christian and still, as a last resort, if ill-fortune or sickness persists, consult a *nganga* and make a suitable sacrifice to his guardian spirits.

---

[1] When a present, whatever form it takes, is made to a spirit, it is set aside in the family's hut and only used on ritual occasions when it is worn by a member of the family.

[2] *Mudzimu* is the singular form of *vadzimu*.

CHAPTER 4

Alien and aggrieved spirits

The *shave*[1] is an alien spirit. The original *shave* was said to be the spirit of a stranger who died in Mashonaland—far from his home, and for this reason his burial lacked the traditional ritual which the Mashona believe every person, whatever his origin, has the right to expect. Consequently *mashave* spirits are essentially restless, they wander about in search of a human host who will accept them.

Their influence is a good one, for they confer a special talent on the person they select; it may be a talent for healing, for hunting, for athletic prowess, or any outstanding skill. Once accepted by its host a *shave* will remain with that person for the rest of his life. The person selected is usually an adult man or woman, though the *shave* does sometimes adopt a child as its medium.

The *nganga* is closely associated with the *shave* cult because apart from the fact that, in many cases, he is himself the medium of a healing *shave*, it is through his divination that it is known that a *shave* wishes to possess a particular host. The first intimation that a *shave* has selected someone is that that person falls ill. Various remedies are probably tried without effect before the family decide to consult a *nganga* who specializes in divination. Besides telling the family that a *shave* is responsible for the illness, this *nganga* will also tell them the kind of *shave* it is, what its requirements are and the type of dress it wishes its medium to wear at ceremonies held in its honour.

[1] *Shave* is the singular form of *mashave*.

39

The relatives return to their village and inform the patient and the other members of the family. The father, or sometimes the wife, of the sick man fills a wooden plate with millet and puts it next to the patient's head. He kneels down and prays to the *shave* spirit saying, '*Shave*, we have been told today by the *nganga* that you wish to possess our son. We accept you. Make him better and we shall brew beer and do all you want us to do'. While the patient begins to recover his normal health, the family are busy procuring the various articles which the *nganga* has told them are favoured by the particular *shave*, at the same time making arrangements for a ceremony to which they invite not only friends and relatives but other mediums with the same type of *shave* as their relative.

When everything is ready, probably a few weeks after the consultation with the diviner, all the guests gather in the evening in the main hut where the ceremony is to take place. An important part of the ritual is the selection of music, for there are special tunes and words to honour each type of *shave*. The guests dance in the open outside the hut until, one by one, all the mediums with the same type of *shave* become possessed by their spirits. As each enters the state of possession, a relative approaches and dresses him in his special attire. The new host joins in the dancing and at some time during the proceedings he also becomes possessed. When this happens, his relatives lead him to the main hut and sit him on a mat while the father kneels before him and over a special pot of beer, called the *musumo*, asks the spirit whether it is indeed a *shave*, what its name is, what talent it confers, where it came from and what it wants. The *shave* replies to each question through its new medium until all present are satisfied that he has become host to a genuine *shave* spirit.

The *shave* cult is in keeping with the general mentality of the Mashona who look for a supernatural cause to explain anything out of the ordinary. They understand and accept

Eldery Shona wearing ritual black shawl prays in his hut to his ancestral spirits

After consulting a *nganga,* a father prays at the foot of a tree to the spirit of his sick child's grandfather

A man with a hunting *shave* demonstrates how he sets his traps

Drummers at a *shave* ceremonial dance

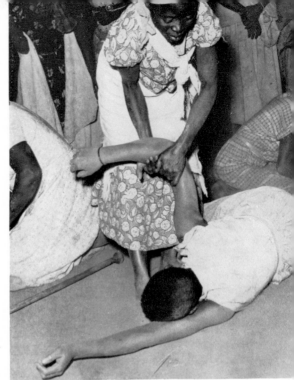

Dancers falling into a state of possession at the height of the music

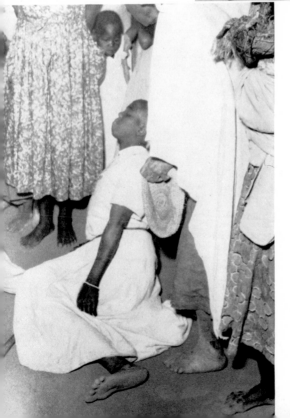

A male and a female medium possessed by *madzviti mashave*. They are dressed according to the requirements of this spirit and wear similar head-dresses

what may be regarded as normal ability, but when a person is outstandingly gifted in a particular field they cannot accept the inherent quality of this gift, because it makes him different from other people. From the Shona point of view Beethoven must have had a *shave* for music, and Bradman one for cricket. An interesting group of *mashave* is the European *shave*. It is said to confer the attributes of a white man and, while in a state of possession, its medium behaves and speaks like a European and is assumed by fellow Africans to have a special understanding of Europeans and is therefore likely to meet with their favour, particularly in the world of business.

Shave are divided into groups depending on their land of origin and the particular attribute they confer. Only one particular *shave* possesses one individual but there is a special bond among mediums whose *mashave* belong to the same group, For instance, at a ceremony in honour of a hunting *shave*, only those with a similar *shave* may participate. They wear the same type of dress, sing the same songs, perform the same dances and generally constitute themselves into a kind of club. Each medium believes that, if he does not fulfil the particular requirements laid down by his hunting *shave*, the spirit will leave him and he will lose his skill in hunting game. It is for this reason that ceremonies are held at regular intervals to honour the *shave*.

A *shave* spirit is sometimes patronal, i.e. it may remain in the same family for generations as we shall see with the healing *shave* of the *nganga*, but the medium of an inherited *shave* is still subject to the same preliminaries of illness necessitating diagnosis by a *nganga* diviner.

From the point of view of the physical symptoms it inflicts, a *shave* differs from the action of a witch, ancestral spirit or aggrieved spirit in that it is never responsible for a death, it only causes sufficient illness to draw attention to its selection of a particular host.

The *ngozi*, or aggrieved spirit, on the other hand, is

responsible for grave illness, and sometimes even death. It originates from a person who has died in anger, or has suffered grave injustice during life. In the previous chapter we saw how a spirit elder—the mother who was ill-treated by her children—acted as a *ngozi* after death. But as a rule, and if suitably honoured and revered, the spirit elder is a contented and protective spirit, while the *ngozi* is always restless and avenging. It may take a long time after death for the aggrieved *ngozi* to become active, sometimes ten or twelve years, but sooner or later it will afflict the person and his family who upset him during life. The first intimation is a severe and usually fatal, illness; if the cause of death is not immediately recognized, another member of the same family is struck down until finally the family realize that a *ngozi* must be responsible. Someone may recall an injustice, or, according to popular belief, the *ngozi* may take temporary possession of one of the family, perhaps a child, and speak to him: 'I am so-and-so. Why did you harm me? I want ten head of cattle to be brought to me in my village.' The family is so thunderstruck at hearing this spoken by one of themselves that they hasten to the *nganga* for corroboration. If the *nganga* confirms the *ngozi's* words, the cattle are taken to the village where the aggrieved spirit lived and given to his descendants. The Mashona say that once the demands of the *ngozi* have been met, the matter is closed and it will not return again to trouble the family.

They believe that an unpunished murder will disturb the spirit of the victim and its *ngozi* will not rest until adequate compensation has been made to the bereaved family. Fear of the *ngozi* is perhaps even greater than fear of the law and therefore acts as a strong deterrent to crime.

Sickness caused by a *ngozi* is one of the most difficult to treat, and only *nganga* highly skilled in this field will undertake to propitiate this spirit—physical treatment often includes inhalations and the spraying of the patient's body with a special mixture.

CHAPTER 5

The witch

The Mashona believe that equally important as a cause of illness, and more frequently the cause of death than the *ngozi*, is the witch. A family is likely to suspect one or the other if the illness is sudden and severe.

Like the people of all other African territories, the Mashona believe that certain people are wicked ard capable of harming others. These are the witches, their intention is to kill, but if their poison is not strong enough or does not operate for long enough, the victim merely falls ill.

The Mashona look upon the *muroyi*, or witch, as a person endowed with the power to manipulate the forces of Nature to the detriment of mankind, but they do not believe they have witchcraft substance in their bodies (an actual physical substance absent in normal individuals—such as described by Professor Evans-Pritchard in the witches of Azande in the Sudan[1]). The Mashona believe that witches are possessed by an evil spirit, which like a healing spirit, can be passed on to others after death. The daughters of a witch do sometimes become *varoyi*[2] during their mother's life, but as a rule the presence of the evil spirit only reveals itself when its host reaches adulthood, and sometimes not until after marriage.

I am told that though any of a witch's kin may inherit her evil, it is generally thought more likely to possess one of her daughters or granddaughters. The first sign of impending inheritance is revealed through dreams.

[1] E. Evans-Pritchard, op. cit. p. 9.   [2] Plural of *muroyi*.

A woman who is believed to be a witch is left unmolested so long as she does not harm anyone, she is even permitted to wander around the village at night. One reason for this, no doubt, is that it is considered highly dangerous to cross paths with a witch unless there is a very good reason for doing so. I have heard it said that a witch can be cured of her evil propensities but I do not think that the Mashona really believe this, they consider that a witch will always remain one and should never be trusted. She enjoys practising evil just as a normal person gets satisfaction out of doing good. It is also possible, as Dr Field observed among the Ga people, for a person to possess the power of witchcraft without being aware of it.[1]

The power of practising witchcraft can also be acquired, although this is extremely rare. The individual who wishes to become a witch apprentices herself to one who gives her the appropriate medicines over a certain length of time, and she must also spend a long period in the company of other witches studying their methods of witchcraft before she acquires the necessary degree of malevolence. But in my experience among the Mashona, unlike Field's findings in West Africa, witchcraft is considered to be almost always hereditary.

The Shona's idea of a witch is similar to that held in other parts of the world. She usually moves around after dark in the company of other witches, and chooses the dead of night to visit graves and eat the bodies of the recently dead. Witches often meet for their discussions at the bottom of river beds, especially at points where streams cross one another. One may bring with her palpable apparatus—calabashes[2] filled with medicines—which she will share with her sister witches. Sometimes a witch will ride a hyena or a wild pig and both these beasts are often found in her home. She is also fond of owls, and when she sets off on her nefarious

[1] M. J. Field, op. cit. p. 26.
[2] Containers made out of horn, shell, or the dried skin of a fruit.

purposes she sends this bird ahead to settle on her intended victim's hut. For this reason, a Shona seeing an owl sitting on his roof, will be thrown into a panic. Or, instead of an owl, the witch may send a snake to crawl amongst her prospective victims. She poisons people by putting medicines in their food or beer. No one ever catches her doing this and she is able to plant the poison wherever she wishes. It is also believed that she can cause death merely by touching her victim or by calling out his name.

Male witches are much rarer than female witches and their practice of witchcraft is different. Instead of moving around at night in the company of other witches and eating the flesh of the dead, they place a poisoned or 'doctored' article along the path the victim is likely to take, but like the female witch they may also poison the food or drink of the person they intend to harm. The Mashona describe these male workers of evil by the same name as a female witch—*muroyi*; in other parts of Africa he is called a sorcerer, a black *nganga* or an evil magician.[1]

Authorities on African studies constantly refer to the sorcerer as a magician who practises evil by using medicines to harm or kill. The Mashona admit the existence of the black magician but, as we have seen, they attribute his power not to his magic, but to his evil spirit. In other words, for the Mashona, the sorcerer is a witch and any so-called *nganga* who uses medicines to practise 'sorcery' is a witch too. It does not matter whether the *nganga* concerned is paid for his services or not—he is a witch and so, in intention, is the person who goes to him for assistance.

Sometimes, according to the Mashona, a good *nganga* becomes a witch because of his desire to become rich, with the result that he starts to harm others for gain. A *nganga* may become angry when he is not paid his fee by a client and

---

[1] M. Gluckman, describes in his book, *Customs and Conflict in Africa*, p. 81., the activities of the male witch among the Zulus.

will threaten him saying: 'If you do not pay my fee you will be sorry'. If after this any member of the client's family becomes ill it is believed that the sickness was brought on by the *nganga* practising *uroyi* (witchcraft) and he is now considered a witch by his former clients because he uses witchcraft against those who do not pay him. A *nganga* who prescribes medicine to procure an abortion is considered to be a witch because he is destroying life, and, for the same reason, so is the *nganga* who gives medicine to induce sterility.

Field agrees with this when, in discussing the subject of witchcraft among the Ga people, she says that the witch-doctor must be scrupulously upright, for 'if he is once guilty of a destructive desire he becomes himself a witch and is powerless to reform'.[1]

The diseases caused by these male witches are usually typical in their manifestations and have special names. The best known is *chitsinga*, characterized by a severe pain in the leg which makes the victim unable to walk. It is believed that a witch who has acquired *chitsinga* medicine looks round for someone who owns a lot of cattle or goats and, in order to obtain some of his wealth, plants the poison on the path leading to the victim's door so that he has to step on it and the poison enters his foot. It is also believed that an ordinary person may buy *chitsinga* from a witch and can himself put it in his victim's path. The man who has developed the pain in his leg consults a *nganga* diviner who tells him that the *chitsinga* was produced by a witch who has designs on his property. Anxious to be rid of the pain, the patient goes to the man who the *nganga* has told him is responsible and gives him some cattle in return for removing the evil. If, however, instead of recovering, the illness continues, it is obvious that the witch has not stopped his malevolent practices and the villagers will now unite against him and demand that he be tried by ordeal; formerly, if he were proved guilty he was killed or driven out of the village. But now the naming of

[1] M. J. Field, op., cit. p. 150.

witches with its consequent trial by ordeal has been made illegal, so today, when a *nganga* diagnoses *chitsinga* in a patient, he does not denounce a particular person but prescribes medicines to drive away the disease. As a result, the patient is no longer obliged to buy off the *chitsinga* 'doctor'.

Another magic medicine known to the Shona is one which prevents a man from stealing the crops of another. If, for instance, a man's mealie crops are particularly good and he is afraid that an evil wisher might help himself to them, he puts a medicine called *rukwa* in his field to protect his crops. Afterwards when a thief comes to filch the mealies, he finds he cannot let go of the cobs, or else that he cannot remove the basket containing the mealies from his head. This type of *rukwa* which helps the victim to find the robber but does not harm him, is believed to be good medicine and is prescribed by a good *nganga*, who thus acts in much the same capacity as a policeman. But there is a type of *rukwa* that causes the thief's abdomen to swell after he has eaten the stolen crops. This *rukwa* is regarded as bad and the *nganga* who sells it is therefore considered a witch.

All my *nganga* acquaintances affirm that they are regularly consulted by patients who believe themselves to be witches. I have questioned them carefully about this and my conclusion is that these patients are probably suffering from a neurosis and are obsessed with a guilt complex. European doctors too are familiar with the patient who is convinced of his wickedness and guilt. No doubt in both cases many of these patients are in a depressive state. Field[1] has observed a similar condition among the Ga people. Many of the Shona who consult *nganga* as self-confessed witches say that they dream of climbing into graves and eating the flesh of the dead, or that they have observed that when they used threatening language towards someone, that person subsequently fell ill or died.

A special rite, well known to practically all the *nganga* I

[1] M. J. Field, op. cit.

have questioned, is used for curing a self-confessed witch. The *nganga* takes the patient to a crossroads, where a black fowl [or a black goat] is given a special medicine. The *nganga* then calls out to the evil spirit to leave his client, and as he does so he releases the fowl, which runs off into the bush, taking the evil spirit with it.

The Shona have been greatly upset by the promulgation of legislation by the Europeans which makes it a serious offence to accuse anyone of being a witch, with the result that instead of being killed or exiled, witches are now allowed to wander about unmolested and, what to the Mashona is an even more serious consequence, they continue to breed witches. This is why, according to them, hundreds of bad people exist all over the land and so much wickedness flourishes. This is a genuine complaint and one greatly fostered by the *nganga*. Counter measures have to be taken and there is a widespread effort to protect everyone against the ubiquitous witch. Charms are purchased to protect the body and pegs planted in the village by the *nganga* in order to safeguard its homes.

I have discussed the question of witchcraft with Africans from all walks of life, many of them highly intelligent people and some of them members of Christian churches, and have found that almost all of them believe in witchcraft. This is less surprising when one remembers that Christianity and the belief in witchcraft co-existed for a long time in Europe. It is because of their fear of witches that the Mashona are so anxious to consult a *nganga* when threatened with sickness or death.

It is not easy to prove that a person is a witch. Badness, or bad behaviour, is not enough. But suspicion arises if, when two people quarrel, one points a finger at the other saying: 'Look out, you will be sorry for this'. If, soon afterwards, the threatened person becomes ill or dies, those who witnessed the quarrel will regard the other party with suspicion, especially if the suspect is seen with others of an equally dubious reputation. Anyone who seems to take pleasure in another's sufferings or misfortune is also suspected of being a witch. But suspicion is not enough: there must be proof that the illness or death was due to witchcraft. A group of people who have witnessed a succession of evil events that cannot be explained and who therefore suspect the action of a witch, will seek confirmation from a *nganga*. He is the person who bears the greatest responsibility for witch finding since it is on his word that the first accusation is made. Since he is not allowed today to name the witch he usually says that a witch is responsible for the misfortune, and advises the family on the general protective measures to stop further witchcraft from entering the village. Every now and then, however, in spite of the penalties, a *nganga* succumbs to temptation and reveals the name of the alleged witch. If this happens, the delegates who have consulted him return to their village and at the dead of night place some ashes in front of the suspect's hut. In the morning the 'witch' sees the ashes and, realizing their significance, protests that she is innocent. The matter is now referred to the chief, and a secret trial by ordeal is arranged. The preparations are left to a man known as a *kapande*, a *nganga* who specializes in this work, and when everything is ready the villagers gather and the accused is told to drink a special medicine. If she vomits she is declared innocent, but if she retains it she is believed guilty. If she suffers from diarrhoea as a result of the medicine, her excreta is examined for evidence of human bones which would prove that she was in the habit of visiting the graveyard and consuming human remains. If the ordeal shows that the accused is innocent, a heavy fine is imposed by the chief on the *nganga* and the family who laid the charge, but if the witch is proved guilty she is driven out of the village.

A few years ago, a chief living about forty miles from Salisbury decided that there were too many witches in his reserve and that the only way to eliminate them was to hold a public ordeal to discover the guilty; he would then exile them from his domain. He arranged for a *nganga* who had a very great reputation for detecting witches to conduct the ordeal, and ordered all his people—men, women and children—to gather in the village on a certain day. No matter where they were working or living, they all had to return to the village to stand their trial; each family also had to hand over all the charms concealed in the eaves of the huts—these usually consist of animal horns filled with preventive medicines to ward off witchcraft. On the appointed day, hundreds of the chief's subjects gathered in the village, their charms were piled together in one enormous heap and everyone in turn stood up in front of the gathering and drank the special medicine. According to custom those who vomited were declared innocent. An extraordinary sequel to the proceedings was the death, within a few hours of drinking the medicine, of four young men who had previously been in excellent health. I was called upon to perform autopsies on them and could find nothing of note to account for their deaths. The pathologists and myself were unable to recognize the nature of the poison used. The *nganga* stood trial in the Rhodesian law courts. He admitted giving the mixture, but claimed that the men who died were witches and that it was because of this that the medicine had killed them, while on the innocent it had no effect except to induce vomiting. The *nganga* was sentenced to four years' imprisonment.

So real is the people's fear of witches that almost every village in the rural districts of Mashonaland, and even many of the African homes in urban areas, are protected against the entry of a witch. Four wooden pegs soaked in the castor oil contents of the *nganga*'s calabash are planted at night at each corner of the village and at the same time every man, woman and child is given a special potion to drink. The pegs prevent the witch from recognizing the village, for when she is out at night on her errands the village looks to her like part of the general landscape. The mixture will also protect the villagers from the harm of any evil person they may meet when they leave their homes and move about the country. This treatment is carried out whenever there is a witch scare in a particular area.

There are probably two reasons for the prevalence of the belief in witches. First, it provides a scapegoat for man's inadequacy, omissions, or failures. Most people are vain and consider themselves capable. Few admit their limitations or inadequacies. Yet each of us constantly fails in some respect or in the ventures we undertake. When this happens the Shona, instead of blaming himself or analysing his actions to learn from past mistakes, blames the witch, the unseen enemy who is everywhere and is always ready to harm a good, honest, unsuspecting person. Their beliefs and superstitions concerning witches also provide the Shona with an object on which to vent their feelings of hatred. This also need not surprise us as even advanced nations act in a similar fashion, they may no longer believe in witches but as a group they still look for a scapegoat. The capitalist, the communist and the Jew have all served as scapegoats in their time.

The second purpose which a belief in witches encourages is good social behaviour. If an individual harms another, breaks laws, or becomes anti-social, he lays himself open to the suspicion of being a witch. If he acquires great wealth whilst those around him are so poor that they can hardly make a living, this not only shows that he is greedy and avaricious, but suggests that his wealth was obtained at the expense of his fellows. The Shona child is indoctrinated with distaste for the terrible attributes of the witch and taught about the awful end liable to befall such persons who are unlikely to get away with their malpractices because of the skill of the *nganga*. Having had this fear instilled in him, the average adult Shona chooses good in preference to evil, tries to behave well and endeavours to conform to the ordinary social pattern of his community. It has to be remembered that in the tribal structure there exists no police force to protect the individual and his property, it is therefore possible that the idea of a witch who is inevitably discovered and punished has a practical value in protecting the community from the would-be evil-doer.

As there is always the fear that an unknown person may be a witch or a wizard, it is considered dangerous to become intimate with any stranger. This fear tends to produce a rather reserved individual who is loath to meddle in other people's affairs. On the debit side, the fear of befriending a stranger may be one of the reasons why charitable bodies are not a feature of African society (although there are probably additional reasons for this). I recently met an African minister of religion who started a home for orphans. The idea of doing something for these children occurred to him one day when he found a destitute child. He felt impelled to take her into his own home, but did not dare to do so before learning the views of his wife and children because amongst Africans, there is, as he put it, 'a great fear of the stranger'.

It is difficult to describe the deep and terrorizing fear of the witch which pervades all African society. Although few Shona today carry out fully their religious practices, the belief in witchcraft is almost universal and shows no signs of abating. Of course, many references to the high incidence of the practice of witchcraft among Africans are made on flimsy grounds. When Africans quarrel, for instance, temper very frequently leads one to accuse the other of being a witch. A common expression is: '*Mutakati:* You are a witch'. But this accusation may mean no more than one European swearing at another and saying 'you so-and-so'. It is interesting to note that the African does not think that a European can be a witch because he believes that the spirit of the white man operates on quite a different spiritual plane to his own.

CHAPTER 6

The scope of the nganga

The *nganga* is the kingpin of African society. Owing to his spiritual endowment he is equally capable of dealing with spirits, whether ancestral, aggrieved or alien and with witches. His scope embraces everything affecting an individual or his family; the only matters outside his jurisdiction are those concerning a group or a tribe, such as the bringing of rain or the selection of a chief. These are the responsibilities of a separate and different group, the tribal spirits, which, as they do not concern the *nganga*, we shall not deal with here.

The *nganga* is essentially a family practitioner and is expected to find the answer to all kinds of personal problems. While he is consulted more often for sickness or death than for any other matter, there are a host of other problems—almost too many to be enumerated—which his clients will ask him to deal with.

He is often consulted about the future: if, for example, a man is about to undertake a long journey, he will ask the *nganga* if he will reach his destination safely, if his mission will be successful, and whether he will be attacked by robbers or wild animals on his way home. The *nganga* may also be consulted by a client who is facing a charge in a law court and is naturally anxious to find out whether he will be acquitted. Another may wish to know whether he will pass an examination; on one occasion I was present when a client asked a *nganga* whether he would pass his driving test. Other clients may want to know whether they will find good jobs.

A boy who wishes to win the love of a girl, but is having little success, will take his problem to the *nganga*, who will tell him where he has gone wrong and what he should do to rectify his mistakes. A man who is disappointed because his children are all girls will ask for a consultation, for the *nganga* has a special medicine to ensure that a pregnant woman will be delivered of a child of the right sex. Some years ago I interviewed a woman *nganga*, a herbalist of high repute and the wife of a chief, who claimed that she could ensure the birth of a child of the desired sex. She enquired about my family, and when I told her that our children were all daughters, she offered to give my wife the appropriate remedy next time she became pregnant.

The *nganga* is also able to take over functions usually associated in other societies with the police; belief in his powers of detection often stops the ordinary person from committing anti-social acts, and the knowledge that he may have dispensed a special medicine to protect a man's property acts as a deterrent to would-be thieves. For instance, on the many occasions it is necessary for a Shona to leave his village, either to go hunting or for some other reason, he may be worried about leaving his wife behind in case some other man enters his hut while he is away and seduces her, or in case she invites him there herself. The *nganga* provides a special medicine known as *runyoka* to safeguard his client's interests while he is away. The husband puts the medicine in his wife's bed and it is said to harm any man who sleeps in it, inflicting him with a dreadful disease. Unlike the medicine called *rukwa* which protects a person's crops and is believed to be prescribed by a bad *nganga* if it harms the thief, *runyoka* is prescribed by a good *nganga* in spite of its painful effects because it is given to protect a marriage and the punishment it inflicts on the adulterer is considered just.

Nganga are also consulted in order to recover a lost or stolen article, although only the more highly skilled diviners are called in for this kind of 'detective' work. I have been told that these *nganga* never fail. Suppose that a man in a Shona village has lost a hoe. He and his friends go to a *nganga* who has a good reputation for divining. The *nganga*, as befitting his high reputation for clairvoyance, identifies his visitors by name and tells them the name of their village and the reason for their visit. The owner of the hoe then asks if the article has been stolen and where it is hidden and he may also ask the diviner to take him to the spot, in which case the *nganga* sets out at once, followed by the deputation who walk behind him in single file. The *nganga* stops at the spot where the hoe is buried. The headman of the area is called as a witness, and all the other inhabitants of the village gather round. The *nganga* turns to the headman and, pointing to the man who stole the hoe, calls upon the headman to ask the accused to admit his theft. The thief, knowing that he is dealing with a person cleverer than himself, usually confesses. At this point, the *nganga* tells the culprit to uncover the hoe and he digs until it is exposed. When the owner identifies his property the *nganga*'s part in the proceedings is over. He goes off saying: 'I have shown you your hoe; my work is finished. I am returning to my village and when the case has been settled you can come and pay my fee.' The thief is fined the amount of the fee.

European society has no one quite like the *nganga*, an individual to whom people can turn in every kind of difficulty. He is a doctor in sickness, a priest in religious matters, a lawyer in legal issues, a policeman in the detection and prevention of crime, a possessor of magical preparations which can increase crops and instil special skills and talents into his clients. He fills a great need in African society, his presence gives reassurance to the whole community and his position will no doubt remain secure so long as the Shona's belief in witchcraft, and his need for an antidote to the witch survive Western education and civilization.

CHAPTER 7

How a nganga qualifies

How does a Shona qualify as a *nganga*? Comparison of the procedures and treatments practised by *nganga* in different parts of Mashonaland show a uniformity which points to at least some sort of basic training.

It is not easy for an African to become a *nganga*—indeed in many ways it is less difficult to qualify at a university where at least medical studies are open to anyone with the necessary entrance qualifications. But an African who wants to be a *nganga* has to show that he is possessed by a healing spirit and that this spirit has been passed on to him by a deceased relative, who was himself a practising *nganga*. A less fortunate person without a family healing spirit will have to prove that a healing *shave* has selected him as its medium.

The initial qualification is therefore considered to be outside the *nganga*'s control and applies to all *nganga*, whether they wish to practise as herbalists, diviners, or specialist diviners. The first intimation of spiritual endowment may be a dream in which the candidate sees the correct medicine to cure a sick person in his village. This often happens when the future doctor is very young, sometimes not more than ten years old. In his dream he is shown the place in the woods where the medicine is to be found, and next morning he goes there and finds the herb. He administers it to the sick person and if he is cured the boy is encouraged to repeat the process the next time he comes across someone who is ill. His dreams may continue in this way for some years until

A *nganga* dressed for the annual ceremony to thank his spirit elder for guiding him in his medical work

He takes part in the dancing, wearing charms across his chest

Above left, neighbouring *nganga* are invited to a thanksgiving ceremony: here the one who is holding the ceremony wears a feathered head-dress and a white shirt; the woman *nganga*, kneeling in front of him, is dressing a dancer

Below left, drums and gourds played during the ceremonial dances

Above, the *nganga* kneels before the pot shelf and offers the first pot of beer to the spirit elder from whom he has inherited his healing powers

After the ceremony in the hut, visiting *nganga* walk through the village carrying their drums

A woman *nganga* attending a similar ceremony wears her ritual dress

he reaches adulthood. He is not, however, a fully-fledged
doctor yet; though he has probably acquired quite a reputation among the local population as a healer, he still has
some exacting procedures to undergo. Sooner or later he will
fall ill himself; then two or three of his closest relations—
such as his father, grandfather, and elder brother—
will seek a diviner to learn the reason for his sickness. The
nganga will discover that his patient has been dreaming
about medicines and treating sick people in his village. In
some cases he will also learn that one of the family's deceased
relatives was a doctor in this life and he will therefore conclude that the dead *nganga*'s spirit wishes his young relative to
practise his profession and accept his healing spirit.

After receiving this information, the relatives take leave of
the *nganga*, and as soon as they reach home, the head of the
family kneels beside the pot-shelf of his hut and clapping his
hands prays to the dead relative's spirit: 'You are the one
who wants this man. I have been told this by the *nganga*'s
hakata[1] which have said that you want him to carry on your
duties. If it is you and you really want him to do what you
did, will you release him from his illness?' If the patient
gets well, his family are delighted and accept his recovery as
indication that the healing *shave* wishes to enter him. I
should perhaps explain here that once a *shave* or alien spirit
has chosen a particular family it is usually passed on from
one generation to another, which is why, as we have already
seen, it can also be described as a patronal spirit; but when
the original entry of the *shave* into a family has become so
lost in the mists of antiquity that the family believes it has
always possessed a healing spirit, then the *shave* becomes
tantamount to a *mudzimu* or ancestral spirit. The *nganga*
who practises through a *mudzimu* is considered to be the most
skilful of all *nganga*.

Theoretically, once the would-be *nganga* has proved that

---

[1] A set of four wooden 'bones' which most *nganga* throw when they
divine.

the healing spirit—*shave*, patronal or *mudzimu*—has selected him as a medium, he is ready to practise his art relying on no more than his spirit to guide him. But in practice most *nganga* spend a period of apprenticeship with another *nganga*.

Let us imagine that it is decided that the young man should receive a course of instruction. The head of the family takes a fowl and, holding it, kneels before the pot-shelf in his hut thanking the spirit: 'I have seen that you are our relative who was a *nganga* in this life and you now wish to work through this person. So I am about to take him to your friend who has a particularly good reputation as a doctor and who will teach him how to carry out all the duties you performed before you died.' He then takes the fowl to the *nganga* to whom he has been advised to apprentice the young man, and the *nganga* accepts it and takes it to his own pot-shelf, where he prays to his spirit: 'This is a friend who has just arrived to be trained by me so that he may become a good *nganga*.' After this the young man's relative returns to his own village to fetch the new medical student so that he can begin his training. He remains in close contact with his teacher, learning his profession and being taught about herbs and their properties and uses; if during this period he dreams about divination, he is taught to divine as well.

When the teacher is satisfied that the young man is ready to set up on his own, he arranges a ceremony for him. He uses his own grain to brew beer and sends word to the young doctor's family and friends to attend the ceremony when the beer is ready to be drunk. Towards sunset on the appointed day, the older *nganga* prays at his pot-shelf: 'I think I have finished my duty. My pupil is now able to do his own work. I am giving him back to his relations and it is now time to tell them what to pay me as my fee.'[1] The guests gather in the *nganga*'s hut for the ceremony. By now the *nganga*-elect

[1] *Musharo* or *badza*.

will have acquired all the equipment[1] he needs to practise his craft as this is the last day he will spend with his teacher.

The older *nganga* spreads a reed mat on the ground and invites the newly-qualified practitioner to sit on it. In front of him on the mat is placed a wooden plate containing his equipment. Two pots of beer are put on the mat as well, and the older *nganga* speaks to the gathering saying: 'I have asked you to come so that you all may know that this man has qualified. He has completed his course of instruction and he has sufficient equipment with which to treat diseases. I am sure that he will carry out his duties well.' At these words, all the men clap their hands and the women shrill[2]. There is music and dancing, and the people begin to drink the first of the two pots of beer.

At dawn the next day, to the accompaniment of music, dancing and singing, the younger *nganga* becomes possessed by his healing spirit and his teacher dresses him in his regalia. He wears a hat[3] and shells[4] round his head, and a striped cloth slung across the front of his chest from one shoulder to the opposite side of his waist, and another black one—which crosses it diagonally from the other shoulder. Round his neck he wears a necklace of red, black and white beads. A large knife is slung over his loins, while in his hand he holds either an animal tail or his axe.[5] Both *nganga* now sit on the mat. Two more pots of beer are placed in front of them and the teacher speaks again: ' I have done my duty by teaching your relative to become a doctor and I now ask for my payment.' After drinking the beer, everyone returns home. The fee given to the teacher depends on the type of training the pupil has received. If he has been taught to

---

[1] This varies according to the requirements of his particular *shave*, but it usually includes the cloths and skins which he will wear round his waist, beads, shells, charms, drum, headgear, axe, animal tail (usually this is from an ox or a game animal) and calabashes for his medicines.
[2] A continuous high-pitched note made at the back of the throat while the hand taps against the front of the mouth.
[3] *Ngundu.*　　　　[4] *Mbamba.*　　　　[5] *Gano.*

treat with herbs, the usual fee is an ox, but if he has been taught to divine (especially if he can divine the causes of death) the fee is two oxen.

When the newly-qualified *nganga* has returned to his own village, he treats any sick people who consult him. A year later he holds a special ceremony called *kugashira unganga* to honour his teacher. In the evening, when the teacher arrives at the village, he goes to his pupil's hut and is given a small pot of beer. The younger *nganga* tells him that this beer was brewed for the *shave* who guides him in his medical work. When the first pot of beer is finished, the young *nganga* calls for a second one. After it has been brought the older *nganga* kneels in front of the pot-shelf and prays: 'We have seen you. This is the ceremony to receive you. You must help this man through whom you appear and carry on your duties in a good way. This man must remain interested in his work.' He claps his hands; the other men also clap and the women shrill. The second pot of beer is shared by all after which they go outside for their porridge and meat. When the meal is over they return to the young *nganga*'s hut and a mat is spread on which two more pots of beer are placed. The older *nganga* explains to the villagers that the ceremony is being held in honour of the *shave* that is about to enter the young *nganga*. The two pots of beer are consumed, and music and dancing starts up accompanied by more pots of beer until the early hours of the morning. By dawn, both *nganga* have become possessed and are clothed in their appropriate garments. A mat is spread out for them to sit on and two pots of beer put on it. The head of the family, the one who took his young relative to the teacher to be trained, now claps his hands and says to the older doctor's *shave*: 'This is your ceremony in return for teaching our relative. An ox is to be killed for your people to eat.' The two *nganga*, both still possessed, are taken to the cattle kraal where they are shown the ox that is to be killed. The teacher turns to his pupil and says: 'This is the animal given to me for receiving the *shave*. We now ask for it to be killed.' After this has been done, the two *nganga* return to the hut and sit on the mat, and two more pots of beer are consumed. If the healing *mashave* spirits wish to speak to the people present, they do so now through their *nganga* hosts.

The meat of the slaughtered animal and also some thick porridge are cooked in the village and served to all the people attending the ceremony in the *nganga*'s hut. Two pots of beer are placed on the mat and the young *nganga* speaks to his senior colleague: 'This is your *jeneko*.[1] We have finished your ceremony.' Both doctors become dispossessed and once again act as ordinary people. Usually, as their spirits leave them, the *nganga* close their eyes, slowly stretching their arms upwards, and lowering them again.

A senior *nganga* is honoured with this ceremony to show his pupil's appreciation of his teaching; after it is over there is no longer any need for the younger man to show special deference to his teacher. When he holds an annual ceremony to thank his *shave*, he will invite the older man together with other colleagues living in the neighbourhood, but he will now treat his teacher as an equal.

According to the Mashona, there is another way a young *nganga* may qualify, and that is by living in a river bed or pool. The Mashona believe that the doctor who learns the practice of medicine in a pool or at the bottom of a river is probably the most highly endowed of all. The Pungwe river running through Portuguese East Africa is a river from which some of the most famous *nganga* are said to have emanated. Edwards[2] relates a legend about a famous *nganga* called Nyamusangudza, who, when he died, requested that his body be thrown into the Winda Pool of the Mazoe River. His wish was carried out but his clothes, regalia and a basket filled with his medicine and equipment were kept and stored in his hut. Months later sickness followed by

[1] The last pot of beer.
[2] W. Edwards, *Native Affairs Department Annual*, vol. 6, p. 23.

death struck his village and the family concerned went to consult a *nganga*. At the same time a great storm arose and a dream came to the nephew of Nyamusangudza. The next morning he could not be found; all his clothes had disappeared from his hut, though his drum remained. People looked for him everywhere, and when they came to the Winda Pool they discovered the missing man's clothes rolled into a small bundle on the bank. They knew at once what had happened: their relative had been called by Nyamusangudza to join him in the pool. For two days the family stayed by the pool beating the drum and calling on Nyamusangudza to send his nephew back with the magic basket which had also disappeared. On the third day, they returned to the village where they found the missing man in Nyamusangudza's hut dressed in the skins and head-dress of the dead *nganga* and with the magic basket in front of him. He had all the medicines from the Winda Pool with him, began to work as a *nganga* among the people and the only roots or herbs he ever used were those that came from the Winda Pool.

The Reverend A. Burbridge[1] in a very fine article on 'How to become a Witch Doctor' describes how a *nganga* called Chiremba qualified by entering a pool. Chiremba had gone to a pool, called Bedzanyaya, to quench his thirst in the company of some girls. When he dipped his calabash into the water, some hidden force attracted him towards the water and as the waters engulfed him he was drawn headlong to the bottom of the pool. When he regained his feet he found himself in a village peopled with incarnate spirits: the realm of the immortal dead. He proceeded to the *dare* of the subterranean village and sat down, as befitted one from a strange country. He was fed with mud and generally made to feel at home, and was then given a hut in which to rest.

While everyone in his real village slept, Chiremba's brother, Watepepa, who believed his brother to be drowned,

[1] A. Burbridge, *Native Affairs Department Annual*, vol. 8, p. 85.

dreamed and heard a voice saying: 'Come, bring hither a fine ox and drive it into our pool that we may restore to you your brother, Chiremba. Your brother is not dead. He is alive but is nourishing himself on mud taken from the floor of our abode.' Everyone decided that the dream was a good omen, so the family drove the ox to the pool and with many heavy blows forced it into the water. As it disappeared beneath the surface accompanied by the beating of drums and the shrilling of women, their brother Chiremba rose out of the water, sitting cross-legged and beating a medicine drum. He had qualified as a great doctor[1]: 'See the credentials bestowed on me by the Immortals. They have crowned me with the physician's chaplet which betokens authority to heal even the most deadly sickness.'

It is only fair to add that I myself have never met a *nganga* who claimed to have received his training in this way.

There are two main types of practitioners among the *nganga*: diviners and herbalists. Distinguishing them according to their functions, one could say that the young *nganga* has a choice of specializing either as a diagnostician or as a therapeutist. The diviner, through the medium of his *shave*, finds out which spirit is responsible for the illness, usually communicating with his spirit through his *hakata* or divining bones. The herbalist, on the other hand, is not concerned with the cause of illness, but only with the treatment of physical symptoms. But he also relies on his *shave* to show him where to find the appropriate herbs, the information usually being supplied to him in dreams. There are, however, some *nganga* who are able to divine as well as to treat with herbs.

There are a few taboos which every *nganga* must learn to honour if he wishes to avoid displeasing his healing spirit. These restrictions apply to both divining *nganga* and herbalist *nganga*. Perhaps the most strictly adhered to of all taboos

[1] In certain parts of Mashonland *chiremba* is used as an alternative for a *nganga*.

is the one forbidding *nganga* to eat goat's meat, unless the animal has been killed in the ritual manner. When the goat's throat is cut, its gullet must not be opened until it is tied off below the line of incision, this is to prevent any of the stomach contents spilling on to the meat and polluting it. To ensure that this is properly done, the slaughterer, after cutting the skin of the goat's neck, inserts his fingers into the wound and probes with them until he has separated the gullet from its attachment on every side. He then ties a tight ligature of fibre round the gullet and cuts right through the original incision, including the vessels above the ligature.

Nganga should, when visiting a strange village, eat only from new plates or ones that have been purified by burning, in case they have been used to eat flesh from a goat that was not correctly killed. The same rule applies to pots in which goat's meat has been cooked, unless, of course, there is a definite assurance from the host that the meat was prepared in the ritual manner. This taboo does not apply to other meat and a *nganga* may partake of it as long as it is not the flesh of his totem animal. [1]

There are also other taboos: one *nganga* told me that he is not allowed to eat the flesh of a chicken taken from below its knee, or its head or stomach.

A *nganga*'s wife is not allowed to lay the *mugoti* [2] on top of her husband's plate of stiff porridge, which she would normally do while preparing the relish to go with it.

---

[1] A tribe is subdivided into sub-tribes or clans and each clan has its own special animal which it may not kill or eat, usually it is a game animal. Members of a clan with the same totem may not marry with each other; they have to marry 'out' (exogamy).

[2] Stick used by the Mashona to stir the mealie porridge.

CHAPTER 8

The herbalist and his medicines

After the divining *nganga* has diagnosed the cause of his
patient's illness and propitiated whichever spirit was responsible or, in the case of a bewitched patient, exorcised the
evil spirit, he passes his patient on to a herbalist *nganga* to
deal with the physical damage already sustained. As the
herbalist has no real knowledge of anatomy or physiology his
remedies are not prescribed for their effect on any particular organ. But though his knowledge of bodily functions is
negligible there are some diseases which the experienced
nganga learns to recognise by their characteristic onset and
symptoms—such as pneumonia, gastro-enteritis in children, leprosy and venereal disease; an experienced *nganga*
will also have some idea of the gravity of an illness. But on
the whole, it is true to say the the *nganga*, unable to link
the symptoms with a particular illness, merely treats the
symptoms.

One type of the *nganga*'s herbal remedies is reminiscent of
the old wives' tales still current in some parts of Europe,
where the carrying of a potato is supposed to cure rheum-
atism or the wearing of a piece of garlic round the neck is
said to prevent a cold. The Shona equivalent is an amulet
often consisting of a herbal preparation suspended on a
string and worn around the neck, arm or waist; it is more
often seen on children than on adults. Many amulets are
intended for the prevention of ill luck, but one used for
curative purposes consists of a small twig, seed or piece of

wood, about half an inch long and an eighth of an inch thick with a fibre threaded through the centre.

Many of the *nganga* herbal remedies are taken by mouth; The most usual is in liquid form and is taken by the patient either mixed with water or in a thin cereal. The selected herb is crushed into little pieces with a pestle and mortar and left overnight to soak in water. In the morning the liquid is ready to be mixed or cooked with cereal into a thin porridge. Like some of our own medicines, this preparation is prescribed twice daily for as long as the *nganga* thinks necessary.

Herbal medicines are also administered by local application. Dried roots are broken into little pieces and crushed into a fine powder which is burnt to ash in a small piece of clay pot. The ash is then mixed with a little oil and the mixture stored in a horn. When required it is rubbed into a small incision in the skin over the painful area. It would appear that in this way almost pure carbon is introduced into the cut. In other complaints, where the symptoms are not localized and the patient appears to be seriously ill, a different form of local application is used: special leaves are soaked for some time in boiling water and the patient is then covered all over with them on the same principle as our traditional mustard plasters. In cases of skin disease, *nganga* use the same treatment, applying warm leaves to the affected part. They very seldom use ointment for the treatment of skin complaints.

Treatment through inhalation is another method prescribed by the herbalist. The roots are placed in water and brought to the boil. A cloth or blanket is placed over the head of the patient and he is instructed to inhale the steam of the boiling mixture. This remedy is used for the common cold, for chest complaints and, perhaps more strangely, for mental diseases.

It is difficult to assess the curative value of these herbs. Some as we have seen in a previous chapter have a magical

connotation, but where there is no magical basis, I believe
there is often an empirical one. There is no doubt that
through trial and error, the *nganga* have discovered that
certain herbs are effective in curing certain symptoms. For
instance, I know a *nganga* who treated her own asthma with
a stramonium[1] leaf and yet she lived in a very primitive
area and had no contact whatsoever with the outside
world. Until many more of these herbs have been scientif-
ically investigated, I feel they should not be dismissed too
lightly as those which have been tried out for years may well
prove to have a specific action.

The herbalist *nganga*'s medicines are not all based on
herbs, some are derived from animals, insects, reptiles, and
rodents. It is impossible to list all the ingredients used.
Often the *nganga* mixes parts of animals, or their excretions,
with herbs and this mixture is either drunk by the patient or
burnt into a powder and applied externally, usually into an
incision made by the *nganga* on the patient's skin.

An interesting feature of these rather complicated medicines is the *nganga*'s fee which varies according to the difficulty with which he obtained the components. One medicine, considered particularly effective by a certain doctor, is
made from lark droppings that have settled at the bottom of
a pool where they become hard concretions; as the doctor
has to dive into the water to look for them, the medicine is
not unnaturally rather expensive.

Quite different forms of treatment are used in cases where
the patient has been bewitched, as here the evil spirit has to
be exorcised and driven out of the sufferer. Usually this is
done by transference—the evil being transferred from the
sick man to an animal or a fowl which is then driven off into
the woods and is presumed to take the evil spirit with it. Or
the *nganga* may take his patient to a crossroads, some way

[1] Familiar all over the world as an ingredient for medicine used in
asthma cases. Cigarettes are also made from this leaf for asthmatic
sufferers.

from his village, and there call upon the spirit to leave the sick man, the evil being left by the side of the road to be picked up by a stranger. The precautions taken by the *nganga* to set loose the evil spirit well away from the patient's village to be picked up by a casual passer-by provide another reason for the African's distrust of strangers.

Transference of evil is also implied when the *nganga* sucks at the affected part of his patient's body. He sucks vigorously with his mouth for a minute or two and spits out a piece of bone, stone or other foreign body, which he has been holding in his mouth. This proves to the patient that the treatment has been successful and has drawn out the disease.

An ancient form of treatment used with great skill by all herbalists is that of the application of the cupping horn, known in Shona as *murumiko*. The *murumiko* is a small horn, its narrow end closed by a piece of wax. The *nganga* makes an incision on the patient's skin, pierces a hole in the wax and applies the wide end of the *murumiko* to the incision. He sucks vigorously through the narrow end and then carefully closes the perforated wax so that a vacuum is maintained. The *murumiko* remains attached to the patient's skin and is left there for about ten minutes. The *nganga* then inspects the colour of the blood oozing from the incision, if it is red he is satisfied that his treatment has been effective, but if it is darkish, he applies the *murumiko* to another site. After two days he repeats the procedure, and again two days later until the blood appears to be normal. It is probable that cupping, like sucking, signifies the removal of evil from the patient's body.

Herbalists are also well-versed in the art of 'scarification': fine linear incisions about half an inch long are made in the skin, usually in pairs on the site of pain. The herbalist is probably unaware that this treatment and that of cupping increase the blood supply to the affected part and for that reason will prove effective in certain complaints; if the patient improves credit will undoubtedly be given, in cases where powdered roots are rubbed into the incision, to the medicines rather than to the cupping.

Another method of exorcising evil spirits, especially when they have caused mental disorders, is the sprinkling of the patient with a special medicine. For this the *nganga* uses the animal tail which he always carries around with him and which is more often considered a badge of office than a part of his medical equipment.

So far these medicines have all been for the treatment of illness, but there is another group of remedies which the herbalist uses and which are known, in different forms, all over the continent. These are the so-called magical preparations and the ones I shall describe are familiar to most natives of Mashonaland. They are obtained from a *nganga* in order to achieve a variety of results: to set up a pleasant and useful social relationship, such as marriage, to restore a relationship that looks like breaking up, to confer a special quality such as strength or courage, to ensure parents that their baby will be of the desired sex, to protect property from thieves and witches and to increase a man's crops.

The Mashona know that emotional upsets and disappointments occur in life but they believe that certain medicines guard against well-defined emotional contingencies. For instance, a woman seeing that her husband's affection for her is waning, cannot explain his loss of interest and suspects that his thoughts are turning to another woman. She goes to a *nganga* and buys a medicine called *mupfuhwira* and adds it secretly to her husband's food. His love for his wife is said to return after he has eaten the doctored meal. Again, if a girl wishes to win the love of the boy she fancies she obtains from a *nganga* special powdered roots known as *zhambwa* and washes herself in water in which the roots have been soaked, with the result that the boy becomes attracted to her. *Chitsini*,[1] a medicine used on confirmed bachelors, is

[1] Composed of the roots of the *ndirire*, the *mundaramo* and the *mushaba-wasikano*.

believed to cure them of their lack of interest and ensure that they become attracted by a woman.

Mangoromera is a medicine that instils courage in the person who takes it and gives him the ability to defend himself and to fight. It is given to boxers, to boys who are being bullied or to anyone who is likely to be mixed up in a brawl. One form is made up of a mixture of the skins of lion, leopard, elephant, crocodile, rhinoceros, a large snake called *shato*, and a fish known as *netemedzi*. The skins are burnt together into ash and half is rubbed into incisions cut over the elbows, the wrists and forearms, and the rest wrapped in a cloth and tied round the biceps of the client's right arm.

Another form of *mangoromera* is prepared by mixing the root and bark of the *munanga* tree with the root of the *murovapasi* tree. The roots are ground to powder and eaten in thin porridge. It is supposed to give the person great strength and abnormal energy so that he can fell trees and undertake other heavy tasks.

In a third type of *mangoromera*, popular with boxers, the *nganga* takes a piece of the heart of a lion, its gall bladder and the gall bladder and part of the brain of a sheep. The ingredients are soaked in water and the liquid is afterwards drunk. The sheep's brain is significant because a sheep can stand many knocks on its head.

In a fourth type of this medicine the roots of the *ndumapasi*, *chifumuro*, *muvanga*, and *chivuno* are mixed together in a bowl of water and left to soak the night before the fight and the next morning the boxer washes his face in the water.

Similar in action to *mangoromera*, but used for children, is *mubikirira* made from the root and leaves of the *mubikirira* and the roots of the *chivuno* and *chifumuro* trees. It is given to children who are afraid to go out and play, and it is said to prevent them from being hurt or bullied by other children. Parents also give it to children who are going to boarding school for the first time.

The herbalist and his medicines

Parents who have too many children of the same sex and wish for a change consult a *nganga* who gives them a medicine called *kupindura*, which is made from the roots of nine different trees[1] cut into small pieces and cooked with mealies. If the couple want a boy they put an axe on the ground outside their hut and as soon as they rise in the morning they must sit on it together for a few minutes. Afterwards they eat the porridge containing the *kupindura*. If they want a girl they sit on a hoe instead of an axe. This performance has to be repeated every day for about two months after the woman has become pregnant.

We have already seen that if a medicine is prescribed in order to help someone and does not harm another or remove something from him, it is said to be supplied by a *nganga*, but if it is deliberately intended to harm a person it is supplied by a 'bad' *nganga* or witch. Some medicines have both a good and a bad form, one example is called *divisi* and is used to protect and increase the crops.

Divisi is used at the present time by many Africans throughout Mashonaland: in the good type the *nganga* mixes various roots with oil and then with the seeds to be planted. When the seeds have germinated and the plants are about two inches high, the *nganga* supplies the owner of the field with a certain powder which he burns on the land in a broken clay pot so that the smoke blows over the whole field. This is believed to prevent witches from getting in and destroying the crop. At harvest time, before he starts reaping, the owner places more medicine on the rock on which he intends to dry his grain. Finally, when the crop has been gathered, medicine is placed in the granary to protect the meal from damage by rodents, pests, insects and witches. This medicine is known as *divisi rakanaka* and is good *divisi*.

Bad *divisi* is called *divisi rakaipa* and in order for it to become effective the owner of the field has to kill one of his, or

---

[1] *Kuuchika, muchika, musiko, mafuta, chikaka musanga, mutsongo, mupinganyika, chipindwa,* and *jekamasasa.*

71

if he is unmarried, his relations' children, either a baby or a child of one or two years old. He must remove certain parts of the body and mix them with herbs. This *divisi* is much stronger than good *divisi* and is believed to increase the crops manifold. Another way of rendering *divisi rakaipa* effective is for the owner of the field to commit incest with his daughter. Both the *nganga* who advises him and the owner of the field are considered witches.

Another kind of medicine which has its good and bad forms is *rukwa*. This is used extensively in Mashonaland and has also been described in other parts of Africa where it bears a different name. Its purpose is to catch a thief when he comes to the field to steal the crop, it makes him unable to move and therefore easy to capture. In another form this magical medicine temporarily blinds the thief, he finds himself in complete darkness and is terrified to move a step and so remains where he is until he is caught.

Yet another type of *rukwa* sends the thief crazy and he remains in this condition until the cause of his illness is discovered and he returns what he has stolen. A special type of *rukwa* can be obtained from the *nganga* to protect fowls from prowlers. It is given to the birds with their food and when one is stolen and eaten by the thief his stomach swells.

If *rukwa* is used not to protect a man's property (in which case it is permissible and dispensed by a *nganga*), but in order to help the thief, it is called *muroyi mbava* and as its name implies can only be procured from a *muroyi*, or witch. It enables a thief to enter a room and steal while the owner goes into a deep sleep and becomes oblivious of his surroundings until after the thief has got away with the booty.

Runyoka is another kind of medicine which like good *rukwa* is prescribed by a *nganga* in spite of the fact that it harms the person it is used against. It is used, as we have seen, by a husband who suspects his wife of being unfaithful. In one

A herbalist *nganga*:
right, using his stamping block to break up roots;
below, breaking a root into smaller pieces with a stone;
foot of page, grinding one of the pieces to fine powder between two stones

Above left, a woman *nganga* sucking out 'the evil' from a patient's forearm

Below left, she spits out 'the evil', usually a piece of bone, as evidence that she has removed the cause of the trouble

Above right, a *nganga* throws his *hakata* for a client

Below right, his equipment, which includes medicinal horns and calabashes, shows that he is a herbalist as well as a diviner

The herbal market in Harare township, Salisbury, where urban herbalists sell their charms and medicines

type of *runyoka* the lover develops a terrible itch all over his body as though he were covered with ants, in another he suffers violent abdominal pains, in yet another he feels a terrible urge for contact with water and is obliged to wash himself continuously.

White's[1] experience of magic amongst the Balovale tribes of Northern Rhodesia is similar to that which I have seen among herbalists in Mashonaland. There it is also divided into two categories—the magic used for malevolent purposes and the magic used for good ones. The medicines too are basically similar to the Shona ones although they differ in components and administration. One of the malevolent ones enables a man to steal, another to harm an enemy. In one type of bad medicine gunpowder is inserted into a human leg bone, and by lighting the powder and at the same time calling out the name of the victim, the latter is supposed to be stricken down. Amongst the good medicines there are some which prevent stealing and some which protect the wearer against enemies. To prevent the entry of witches into a village, doctored wooden pegs are placed in the ground in much the same way as it is done in Mashonaland.

The magic of the Bemba as described by Moore[2] is also comparable. He gives some good examples of sympathetic magic; for instance, medicine to ensure a good journey is made from portions of the brain and heart of an animal mixed with a root that sends out runners (*mweke mweke*) thereby ensuring that the person who takes it will never lose his way. Another interesting example is prescribed for a man who is underweight: the medicine is called *chisambi* and is made from a chameleon, a small animal which is able to hunch its body and blow itself out and appear much larger than it is. The python, linked with strength and madness in

[1] C. M. N. White, *Africa*, vol. 18, p. 81, 'Witchcraft, Divination and Magic amongst the Balovale Tribes'.
[2] R. J. B. Moore, *Africa*, vol. 13, p. 211.

fight, and known to kill many animals, is prescribed in order to produce extra power in battle: an extract of the python's heart is rubbed into an incision cut in the warrior's arm. The python is also used by the Bemba witch to mix with other medicines and cause death in the house of an enemy.

CHAPTER 9

The diviner: his hakata and spirit possession

A fascinating feature of the divining *nganga*'s equipment is his *hakata*, the bones or dice he casts to divine the cause of sickness, or to find the answer to other problems which his patient brings him.

Hakata may be fashioned from pure bone or ivory, but usually they are carved out of a special wood, chosen because it is hard and will not crack. The *nganga* does not normally make his own *hakata* but buys them from men known for their skill as wood carvers.

A set consists of four *hakata* which are known by the same names throughout the continent, each has a different design on one face only of the bone. The four designs are practically identical throughout Africa, and it is a great pity that the *nganga* do not seem to know anything about their origin. One *hakata*, called *chitokwadzima*,[1] has a rough outline of a crocodile—the symbolism of river dweller and water suggesting purification and cleanliness. A second *hakata*, known as *chirume*, is identified with the male sex, a third, called *nhokwara*, with the female. The sexual connotation of these two bones is generally accepted by all the diviners I have met but for the fourth bone, *kwami*, I have not been able to discover any single meaning, its interpretation varying from one diviner to another.

Because the designs on the *hakata* are so rudimentary, it is very difficult to make out what they are supposed to repre-

[1] Or *ngwena*, the Shona word for a crocodile.

sent and consequently many different theories have been expounded by students of the subject in Southern Rhodesia. Edwards[1] suggests that the *hakata chirume* stands for youth and young manhood, *chitokwadzima* for manhood and strength, *nhokwara* for girlhood, joy and pleasure, and *kwami* for womanhood and maternity. Tracey[2] agrees with Edwards that all four 'bones' carry a sexual connotation. The two male *hakata*, he says, portend things associated with man such as duty, striving, danger, ill luck, work, disappointment; whereas the two female *hakata* denote the opposite—respite from duty, rest, safety, good luck, play, comfort and fulfilment of desire. He suggests that the design at the lower end of *nhokwara* represents the female genital organs, that on *chirume* the male, that possibly the design on *kwami* is meant to represent the breasts of a woman, and that the crocodile tail of *chitokwadzima* is another phallic symbol.

Von Sicard[3] believes that the four *hakata* represent 'the total of humanity in its comprehensive life and as such give a very early stage of human mythical conception: *kwami* stands for motherhood, *nhokwara* a marriageable girl, *chirume* the essence of man, and *chitokwadzima* an old person'.

A diviner cannot use a set of *hakata* when he first gets it because new *hakata* are said to be 'blind' and unable to 'see the truth'. The set must first be treated and each *nganga* has his own special ritual for this purpose. Some chew certain roots and spit on to the *hakata* which are then placed in the doorway of their huts and covered with a pot. They are left there overnight and in the morning are considered ready to 'speak'. One *nganga* I know takes his new set to a crossroads to spit the special medicine on to them and leaves them there all night. But this treatment by itself is still not sufficient, each time the *nganga* divines he must chew another special root and again spit on the *hakata*. The methods of

[1] W. Edwards, *Native Affairs Department Annual*, vol. 7, p. 16.
[2] H. Tracey, *Native Affairs Department Annual*, vol. 12, p. 23.
[3] H. Von Sicard, *Native Affairs Department Annual*, vol. 36, p. 26.

'breaking in' new *hakata* vary geographically; in one place I know of the *nganga* sprinkles his *hakata* with a mixture of special roots and the faeces of a lark.

Since only one surface of a *hakata* is marked, and the others are plain, the diviner's set of four bones can fall in sixteen different combinations. Each time the doctor throws his bones he quickly looks to see how they have fallen, calls out the name of the combination and explains its meaning in reference to the particular question asked. A few of the combinations are considered to denote an excellent outlook, others portray a much less favourable one, and two or three imply a very serious prognosis, even death. When watching a diviner throw his bones, one cannot help being impressed with the speed at which he throws them down and picks them up. It is done so quickly that one sometimes wonders whether he really reads them or whether he merely says what he feels his client expects to be told.

In the past few years I have made a special study of a section of the Makorekore, a large group of Shona-speaking tribes who live in the northern part of Mashonaland. Among the Makorekore most *nganga* use a different kind of *hakata* consisting of half seeds of the fruit of the *mungoma* tree. The seed is very much like an ordinary peach seed in shape, size and general appearance. The seed is not, however, simply collected from the fruit itself, it has to be recovered from the droppings of an elephant. The whole seeds are gathered and cleaned, then bisected and boiled in a clay pot filled with castor oil. After they have been boiled a small hole is made through the centre of each seed, and six of them—a set—are strung together by a thin leather string and stored in a small goatskin.

This set of six half seeds, like the new *hakata* bones, cannot be used to contact the spirits until they have been ritually prepared in a ceremony called *kufara*. The *nganga* selects a path across which the root of a tree passes and cuts off a small piece of the root and takes it home with him. The day after the new moon appears, he chews the root and spits it on to the *hakata* seeds. This procedure has to be repeated each month at the same time.

To throw the *hakata*, the *nganga* holds two of the set in the palm of one hand and the remaining four in his other palm. After he has asked a question concerning his client's problem, he opens both hands at once and the *hakata* fall to the ground.

If all six *hakata* fall with their convex surfaces upward, the combination is called *yakunama*.[1] One convex seed and five concave is *chirume*; two convex and four concave is *makomana maviri*;[2] three convex and three concave is *mutatu*;[3] four convex and two concave is *nokwara maviri*; five convex and one concave is *karomo*; all six concave is *zaru*.

To show how these combinations work out in practice, let us imagine that the *nganga* starts by asking if his client's sickness is caused by a *mudzimu*, or ancestral spirit. If *makomana maviri* turns up this means that the grandfather's spirit is the cause of the trouble, but if *mutatu* appears, the grandmother's spirit is to blame. The *nganga* now has to throw again to confirm his diagnosis and in this context, *mutatu* always signifies agreement and confirms the previous throw while *zaru* means disagreement and the previous throw has to be disregarded.

If the *nganga* gets no satisfactory answer about the *mudzimu* he proceeds to the next type of spirit. He asks: 'Is it a *shave* spirit?' and if *chirume* falls, this answers his question in the affirmative and he can now proceed to identify the particular type of *shave*, naming different *mashave* until he gets confirmation with *mutatu*.

After he has identified the spirit which has caused the

[1] Also known as *mashangure*.
[2] Another name for this throw is *sekuru*, the Shona name for the grandfather's spirit.
[3] Also known as *matokwadzima*.

illness, the *nganga* still has to find out, by the same process of question and elimination, what the particular spirit wants in the way of ritual or propitiation in order for the patient to recover. But if *mudzimu, shave* and *ngozi* spirits have all been eliminated as causes, the *nganga* finally has to ask the bones if a witch is responsible for the illness—a throw of *yakunama* indicates assent and in the old days, the *nganga* would have gone on throwing the *hakata* until the bones revealed the name of the witch.

Not every diviner uses the *hakata*; for instance, I have never yet met a woman who did, and I am told that if she were to do so she would become deranged. *Nganga*, of both sexes, who divine without *hakata* pass into a trance during which the divination is done by the *shave* that possesses them; perhaps one should stress here that though diviners who use the *hakata* are not possessed by their healing spirits when they throw the bones, they believe implicitly, as do their clients, that the *hakata* are ' turned ' by spiritual influence.

Nganga who divine in a state of possession fall into different groups according to the type of *shave* that possesses them. We have already seen that a *shave*, however long it may have remained in one family, originally came from an alien spirit. These alien spirits are grouped, like clans, according to their geographical origin. Each clan or group of *mashave* have characteristic requirements which their human hosts must fulfil in order to please them. Only one healing *shave* possesses one human host, but the *nganga* who are possessed by *mashave* of the same group have the same kind of relationship to each other as members of a clan, they wear the same clothes when they divine and carry out the same kind of ritual.

Some of the *mashave* that operate in this way are: *Masangano* from the Shangaan tribe in the Transvaal, *Mazenda* of Matebele origin, *Murungu* of European origin, *Sena* from Portuguese East Africa, and *Marozvi* from the Fort Victoria area. *Nganga* possessed by these *mashave* usually confine their divination to simple matters, they do not, for instance, divine on important matters such as the cause of death, but refer their clients to specialists in divination who can usually claim a *mudzimu* as the origin of their healing spirit.

An idea of the dress to which *mashave nganga* have to conform can best be given by describing the requirements of some of the groups I have mentioned. *Mazenda nganga* wear two blue cloths diagonally across the chest and back from each shoulder to the waist, their head-dress (*ngundu*) is made of white and black feathers, and they wear a *wizi* which is a metal structure, golden in colour, over the breastbone. To complete the *Mazenda* requirements, strings of red and white beads, plaited together, are worn around the forehead and the back of the head.

The *Marozvi mashave* like their mediums to wear a black cloth slung diagonally across the chest, a *ngundu* of black ostrich feathers and a string of black beads around the waist. The *nganga* must also wear a calf-skin skirt decorated with golden-coloured beads and must carry an axe instead of the more usual animal tail.

The *Sena mashave* wear strings of twisted fibres from the *mushavi* or *matzami* tree across the chest and a special headdress, called *ndyukura*, which is a tiny hat of cock and ostrich feathers covering only part of the head. Two pieces of leather hang from the waist, back and front[1] and the medium carries an axe known as *tsomo* which is similar to the more traditional *gano*.

As the *Murungu mashave* are of European origin, their requirements are those of a white person—their mediums must wear a hat, a pair of trousers, a white shirt, a tie, and shoes, preferably white tennis shoes. They carry a walking stick and often smoke a pipe. The mediums who, strangely enough, are usually women, speak a kind of pidgin Bantu, sometimes called kitchen kaffir; when possessed by their

[1] This garment is called a *madumbo* and is made from the skin of a large spotted genet.

A diviner specialist with eight sets of *hakata*

A set of wooden *hakata*
above: *nokwara* and *chitokwae*
below: *chirume* and *kwami*

A set of *mungoma* seeds

shave they ask for raw eggs and any type of food eaten by Europeans and before eating it will wash their hands, head and face. They frequently rise and jump about during possession and mimic the European with exclamations such as 'my boy, my boy'.

Each of these *shave nganga* has an assistant through whom all messages are conveyed from the patients to the *nganga*. This assistant, or acolyte, may be the husband or wife of the *nganga* or a close friend with whom he can work in harmony. Such an intermediary is necessary because when the *nganga* emerges from his state of possession he is unaware of what took place during the trance, and of what the spirit said through his lips.

Spirit possession is probably best manifested by Africans reared in their natural environment, the more they adopt Western culture and education the more difficult it becomes for them to enter this state. At the tribal ceremonies I have attended in Mashonaland the possession of the medium by his spirit has always followed a stereotyped pattern, whether the person is possessed by an alien (*shave*) spirit or by a tribal (*mhondoro*) spirit.

At the beginning of the ceremony, the medium sits quietly on a mat while music is played and the people dance; he appears to take little notice of what is going on around him. But, after a time, as the music and dancing become more insistent, he rises and joins the dancers until, after a variable time, usually about one to two hours after the music has started, his muscles begin to stiffen. He jerks his arms rapidly backwards and forwards in time with the music and utters sharp monosyllabic cries, such as 'Eh! Eh!' If, however, as occasionally happens, he has remained seated, he may move forward on his buttocks, jerking his whole body in a kind of infantile crawl. At this point the music increases in vigour and tempo and the medium passes into what appears to be a trance; but just before this happens he may fall to the ground shaking violently in which case his assistant will rush up to prevent him from hurting himself. When he has become quiet again—that is when his spirit has taken full possession—the assistant robes him in his special clothes.

During possession, a medium's behaviour depends on the kind of spirit that possesses him. If it is a female spirit, the medium will walk, talk and gesticulate like a woman, but if it is a male spirit the medium, if she happens to be a woman, will conduct herself like a man, talking in a gruff voice and perhaps smoking an African type of cigarette. Sometimes when a medium of the tribal spirits falls possessed, he utters guttural noises, like a lion's grumbling and will repeat similar leonine noises at intervals throughout the period of possession. A medium who becomes possessed by a baboon spirit— a very common form of tribal mediumship in Mashonaland —will behave like a baboon. The ability to become possessed at these ceremonies is shown by children as well as adults, and I have seen girls of twelve and fourteen going into this trance-like state. Some mediums, on the other hand, appear no different to the spectator when they are possessed, they remain seated while the music plays and even appear listless, their quietness or activity is believed to depend on the impression the spirit wishes its host to convey. But whether they remain quietly seated, or talk, move about and answer questions, the mediums are believed to be oblivious of their surroundings and unable to remember what took place while they were possessed. Not long ago, some Africans, on a charge in the Southern Rhodesian courts for spreading unrest amongst their fellow Africans and encouraging non-co-operation with the government, claimed in their defence that they were tribal mediums and were not responsible since they had no recollection of what they had said.

The state of possession may last for a number of hours and when it comes to an end the departure of the spirit is not accompanied by movements as spectacular as those which heralded its entry. Impending departure is signalled by the medium's yawning and stretching his arms outwards and upwards as if awakening from a deep sleep. He often comes out of his trance with long sighing respirations and prolonged and deep inspirations. I once saw an interesting awakening by a middle-aged woman who was possessed by a Matebele spirit. At the end of the ceremony, at 5.30 in the morning, the head of the village informed the spirit that the last pot of beer was about to be consumed. The medium got up and joined in the dancing for a few minutes, then she pulled a handful of long thatch from the roof of a nearby hut, lit it at a small wood fire and walked amongst the people waving the burning grass above her head. Finally she threw it away, rushed forward a few yards with arms outstretched and then her whole body gradually stiffened. Some women hurried up to her to prevent her from falling and within about five seconds she was herself again.

To return to the *nganga* and his state of possession, I have been told by some *nganga* that the more experienced a doctor is the more easily he falls possessed and the more readily the spirit leaves him. The learner, or recently qualified *nganga*, is likely to become physically exhausted at both these stages, though at some ceremonies I have attended, experienced *nganga* also seemed to undergo a considerable amount of physical and mental tension before falling possessed and appeared to be in a state of complete exhaustion when the spirit left them. I remember one female *nganga* falling prostrate on her face at the end of a ceremony, beating the ground with her hands. But I have also seen experienced *nganga* become possessed very easily with only a little music or simply by his acolyte clapping his hands and calling for the spirit to enter him.

I have suggested elsewhere[1] that the state of possession is possibly related to a prehypnotic state or one of high suggestibility, and Dr M. J. Field, who has had considerable experience with spirit possession among the Ga people, also

[1] *Shona Ritual, Shona Religion.*

recognizes the trance as a state of hypnosis. 'It is clear,' she writes, 'that the disassociated state has some ground in common with sleep-walking and hypnosis.' She describes the first indication of the state of possession as a form of 'fit' characterized by excitement of short duration, not often lasting more than two or three hours: 'The person is speechless, sometimes fidgeting as in an insulin stupor, and usually looks oppressed. He sits head-in-hands or huddles himself on the ground with his head over his knees or, if he is standing, he may sway with drooping eyelids as if asleep on his feet.'[1]

When the medium falls possessed, the hyperkinetic state is over and the individual becomes to all intents and purposes quiet and calm. We can say that the 'possession fit' as described by Field, is over.

The *nganga* may remain possessed by his spirit for hours—sometimes ten hours or more—and the spirit will speak through him at convenient intervals. Those seated round him may simply listen to what the spirit has to say or they may put questions to the *nganga*. When he is not engaged in talking or answering questions, he takes part in the dancing. There are times, of course, when these states of possession at ceremonies are feigned. For instance, on more than one occasion, when everything seemed to be genuine and according to type, I have noticed that the possessed medium would, at a suitable moment, accept a tip of money from someone, which he quickly put into his pocket. And I have to admit that I have myself been taken in by a *nganga* over-anxious to impress me with his powers. Once I visited one who lived in a reserve 30 miles from Salisbury; I arrived there with an African nursing orderly and was met on the outskirts of the village by some of the *nganga*'s family, who escorted us to him. He was dressed in the clothes of a woman, and walked and held himself in a womanly fashion. I was told that his healing spirit belonged to a woman and that it would only possess

[1] M. J. Field, *Search for Security: an Ethnopsychiatric Study*, pp. 55–65.

him if he wore female attire, and played a musical instrument made out of a gourd. While apparently in a state of trance, he sat down on a mat with his male acolyte next to him and began to speak. He asked me how many daughters I had. In reply I asked him what he knew about my daughters and he told me that I had three girls, that the eldest was in England and that her name was Joy. I must confess that hearing this from a man I had never met impressed me tremendously. I said no more, and he proceeded to divine on some other matter. On the way home I asked the orderly how the *nganga* knew the name of my daughter and that she was in England, and was most disappointed to learn that as soon as we had arrived in the village he had asked the orderly about my family and what they were doing.

It would be difficult in the present state of our knowledge to claim that the mediums in a genuine disassociated state are able, as Dr Field suggests, to concentrate better and draw conclusions more ably and even to penetrate the future. She also suggests elsewhere a parallel between the Western person who claims to have solved a problem in his sleep and the *nganga* who claims that he has seen in his dreams when a patient is going to visit him, what his ailment is and how it can best be treated. She may well be right—it is generally admitted that the more primitive the individual, the more receptive and active is his unconscious mind.

CHAPTER 10

Consultations and fees

The normal procedure when a member of the family in Mashonaland falls ill is to consult first a diviner who will diagnose the cause of the illness and then, on his advice, a herbalist who will treat the symptoms with his medicines.

The patient himself is not present at the consultation with the diviner which takes place in the *nganga*'s village and is attended by one or more of the patient's relatives. The reason it is unnecessary to see the patient is that the family spirits which the *nganga* will contact in order to find out which has been offended are shared by all the members of the patient's family.

If a child is ill, the father usually goes alone to see the *nganga*, but if he suspects that the illness is due to some serious cause, such as a witch or an aggrieved spirit, he will bring two or three other members of the family with him to act as witnesses, probably the mother of the sick child and one or two of its uncles. If a wife is ill, her husband goes to the diviner, but if he is told that one of her ancestral spirits is involved, he has to inform one of her relations, preferably her father, who then visits the *nganga* to answer questions about his family spirit and to learn what must be done to propitiate it, because, of course, only blood relations share the same *vadzimu*. For this reason, when a husband is ill, his wife nearly always takes his elder brother with her to the consultation.

Whoever the patient, or whatever the number of the delegation, the consultation proceeds along roughly the same lines. The family wait outside the hut while the *nganga* dresses himself in his divining regalia. When he is ready he leads the delegation to a particular tree just outside the village. This is his consulting room and is called the *dariro*. The delegates sit under the tree with their legs stretched out facing the *nganga*. No one may cross his legs when sitting opposite the doctor, who himself sits with his feet crossed and knees far apart. The head of the family hands the diviner a coin.[1] This is the *nganga*'s fee which he accepts and places beside him; he chews a little medicine and quickly spits it out on to his *hakata*. The procedure at this point may differ as some diviners throw the bones themselves, others hand the head of the family delegation a set of four bones and ask him to cast the first throw. Before he throws, he tells the *nganga* the reason for the consultation. The diviner glances quickly at his client's throw, picks up the bones, shakes them in the palm of his hand and throws them down, chanting to his spirit as he does so and asking it to tell him whether the spirit whose name he calls out has caused the illness. When the *hakata* have confirmed which spirit is responsible the relatives ask what it needs in order to be appeased and again the doctor confirms with his *hakata* whether it wishes for beer to be brewed, a beast to be named after it, or a gift such as a blanket. Finally the family spokesman asks if the patient will recover and the *nganga* repeats the question as he throws the *hakata* for the last time. The fee for an ordinary diviner, like the one described above, is paid in advance with the coin handed over by the leader of the delegation before the *hakata* are thrown; this kind of divining is known as *kuchenura*. But when a family delegation consults a *nganga* who divines without *hakata*, the procedure and the fee are slightly different.

[1] Formerly a bangle (*ndarira*) was given; the amount of the fee depends largely on the reputation of the diviner and the seriousness of the illness. For simple divination the fee is quite small.

The fee is handed to the *nganga*'s assistant, it might consist of a hen, a chicken, a bracelet, or a small coin. The assistant claps his hands to induce the *shave* to enter his *nganga* and says: 'We have this man who has come with his troubles so may you enter your medium and tell him why these troubles have beset him.' Another way of inducing the *shave* to possess his host is for the assistant to present the *nganga* with a little snuff box[1] on a wooden plate on which he also places the divining fee.[2] On the other hand, I have met *shave* doctors whose spirits would only enter them after they had fulfilled the most peculiar requirements like the male *nganga* mentioned earlier who had to dress in woman's clothes and behave like a woman.

When the spirit has entered the *nganga*, the assistant again claps his hands and addresses it: 'This is the *chimuti* brought by this person so that you can find out the cause of all his troubles.' The *shave* now speaks through the *nganga* about all that it 'sees'; it also asks questions, always addressing the assistant who interprets its words to the deputation. Because certain healing *shave*, depending on their country of origin, speak strange tongues, the *nganga* may divine in an African dialect, in Portuguese, or even in English; the assistant, having always worked with the *nganga*, is expected to be familiar with the *shave*'s language.

The *shave*'s questions usually concern religious ritual. Has the family buried a certain deceased relative in the correct manner? Has it prayed to or remembered its ancestral spirits? It is probable that in the course of these questions and answers a hint is given by the family of what they particularly fear or suspect is the cause of the illness. A consultation usually lasts about an hour, but it may take much longer and go on for as long as three or four hours, because the family is naturally anxious to be quite sure that the *nganga*'s diagnosis is correct. Once the *nganga* is in a state of possession, he may see three or more family deputations, one after the

[1] *Nhekwe.*   [2] *Chimuti.*

other, his assistant dealing with the preliminaries and the fees.

Besides these two types of diviners there is a third—the specialist diviner known in Shona as *muvuki*. Because of his greater skill and familiarity with the spiritual world he is paid a much larger fee.

Divination of the cause of death is considered to be the specialist diviner's greatest service to his people. Because of the ever-present fear of witchcraft, death is rarely accepted as due to natural causes; this fear leads to the belief that one death in the family will be followed by another unless the witch's evil is exorcised. However, in the case of elderly people, the *muvuki* does often reassure his clients by telling them that death is due to natural causes.

The approach to a *muvuki* and the subsequent consultation are conducted in a different way to those of the ordinary diviners. As soon as possible after a death in the family, the near relations set off for the *muvuki*'s village. When they reach the outskirts, the head of the deputation halts and shouts out: '*Takutuka chiremba*': 'We have scolded you, doctor.' No explanation of the use of those words is known. As soon as he hears this greeting the *nganga* replies: 'I have seen you', and goes out to meet his clients. After this he returns to his hut to dress in his ritual clothes and then joins them again. Without waiting for them to speak he tells them the reason for their visit. Indeed, he is supposed to be able to tell them the name of the person who died and all the details of the death. If what he tells them is not correct, the family immediately lose confidence in him, and go elsewhere. For, in their opinion, if he is really a diviner for determining the cause of death, he will make no mistake. When the family are satisfied with these preliminaries they are taken to his *dariro*. But before he starts to divine he will ask for his *gogodzero* (the first part of his fee). This used to consist of a copper bracelet or a hoe, though today it is more likely to be two new hoes or three fowls.

When all are seated under the tree and the leader of the delegation has handed the *gogodzero* to the *nganga*, he says: 'We have come to you, *chiremba*, to hear the cause of our dear relative's death.' The *nganga* picks up a set of bones and each time he throws, addresses the bones in a formula starting with the same words: 'These people have come to me, a son of a *nganga*, and want to be told what killed their relative . . .' The *muvuki* plays his *hakata* in much the same way as the ordinary diviner, going through the same procedure of questioning the bones and interpreting their answers.

After divination, the *nganga* asks for the *fuko*,[1] and is given either another new hoe or a fowl. He then asks for his final fee, the *mhenhu*, and receives a copper bangle which is to pay for the piece of chalk with which he proceeds to mark one of his *hakata* and afterwards the foreheads of each of the relatives. This chalk mark shows everyone they meet that the *nganga* has given the family the cause of their relative's death and that they are satisfied that what he has told them is the truth.

A specialist diviner is also consulted in the case of lost objects or suspected thefts and in some cases their fees may be very high indeed and consist of an ox or a cow, but in these cases the fee is only paid after the recovery of the lost property.

The herbalist, unlike the diviner, has to see his patient. He does not carry out a physical examination, but relies on the patient's history of his illness, his description of the pain and the visible signs. If the patient is well enough he visits the *nganga* in his own village. Otherwise the *nganga* comes to him and if he is very ill will remain with him during the

[1] This is the cloth in which the dead person was buried, the word is used here metaphorically as part of the *muvuki's* ritual and signifies the second part of his fee.

critical phase of the illness leaving him only when he is
satisfied that the patient is improving and that the relatives
understand his instructions about how the herbal remedies
must be prepared and administered.

When a family, including the patient, comes to consult a
herbalist, the head of the family gives him a fowl or a small
hoe, but when the herbalist is called into a home he is presented with a bangle or bracelet[1] to compensate him for
having left his own home. As soon as he enters his patient's
hut he calls for *kuchenjedza murwere*. This is a gift rather than
a fee and usually consists of a fowl. This present allows the
herbalist to approach his patient. Usually as soon as he has
given the necessary treatment and prescribed and applied
any further remedies, the *nganga* returns to his own village
where he waits until he hears that the patient is well again.
He then returns to the patient's village to determine whether
or not a proper cure has been effected. It is only after the
full recovery of his patient that he asks for his *musharo*[2] or fee.
This varies according to the nature and severity of the illness
and also the difficulty with which the ingredients of the
remedy were obtained. For a serious illness, the herbalist
may ask for a goat, for a minor ailment only a cock. Nowadays payment is made in money, but in remote areas the
nganga is still paid in kind in the traditional manner.

Two diseases which, if cured by the herbalist, call for the
highest payment are epileptic fits and leprosy. The fee for
their successful treatment is an ox. Epilepsy is treated in the
nganga's village, but leprosy, which is recognized as a contagious disease, is always cared for outside his village, in a
small shelter called a *musasa*, which is usually situated within
a circular enclosure.

Although it is usual, and more correct, to consult a diviner

[1] *Rusumuro.*
[2] Also called *badzarako* and *shano*, these are his fees for the cure: the
fees paid before this, that is when the family first call him in, are more
in the nature of chemist charges for collecting the herbs and preparing
them.

before going to a herbalist there are exceptions to this rule. If a herbalist *nganga* has a reputation for curing a specific disease, the family may go straight to him. The case of epilepsy is an instance. Again, if an illness, such as a very severe headache, or an attack of acute abdominal pain, strikes very suddenly, the family will call on a herbalist first for a remedy to alleviate the pain and afterwards consult a diviner about the cause. Or if a patient becomes much worse and seems to be losing ground, several *nganga* may be consulted regardless of whether they are herbalists or diviners.

A good herbalist, when he sees that his treatments are not proving effective, usually advises the patient to consult another. He may tell him the name of one who has a good reputation for his particular illness and the patient is free either to accept his advice or to find someone himself. Sometimes, too, the patient may become dissatisfied with a *nganga*'s treatment and go to another of his own accord.

Besides treating individuals, the herbalist *nganga* has a more general duty to perform, one which affects the whole community. He may be called upon by the chief of a district to protect the inhabitants from epidemics believed to be caused by witchcraft.

This is an interesting ceremony which is worth describing. The day after his arrival in the chief's village, the *nganga* prepares some thin porridge at dawn and adds a little of his special medicine to it. When it is ready he puts it in a winnowing basket outside the main hut, and all the villagers are ordered to come and drink some of it. The *nganga* stands next to the medicated porridge holding in his hand his whisk made from an animal's tail. As each villager moves up to the *nganga*, he closes his fists, dips them in the porridge and licks it off his hands, while the *nganga* dips the tail into a small clay pot of water and sprinkles him. Everyone in the village, men, women and children must go through this ceremony. In addition, the headmen of every other village in the chief's domain also have to be present and each is given a little of the medicine in a calabash to take back to his village, where he must spread it by dipping his finger into the porridge and smearing it on the threshold of every hut. To make certain that witchcraft has been completely eradicated and to prevent it from re-entering the village, the *nganga* plants little wooden pegs at intervals on the boundaries of the chief's territory. When all this has been done and his task is completed he returns to the chief for his fee. This is usually a cow and a calf, or the equivalent in money. The Mashona believe that after such thorough preventive measures it is unlikely that an epidemic will break out again in that district for many years.

The *nganga* may not force his clients to pay their fees. This stricture is not entirely disinterested because were he to threaten them and at a later date a calamity struck a member of the client's family, they would certainly remember the threat and impute the *nganga* with witchcraft. But most *nganga* feel that they are entitled to protect themselves by refusing to treat members of a family who have failed to honour their obligations. The amount or kind of fee is left entirely to the *nganga* concerned, in the case of the herbalist *nganga* the fee is only paid after he and the family are satisfied that a cure has been made. If the family is unable to meet his fee he is perfectly willing to wait until they can afford to pay him. This, and the fact that *nganga* are prepared to call in other *nganga* for consultations, or send their patients to a *nganga* specialising in their particular complaint, points to quite a high code of ethics among 'witch doctors'.

Offering to a spirit elder

My excuse for describing this ceremony[1] in some detail is that it is a very important event in the lives of the Mashona and it also explains how the *nganga*'s instructions are carried out when he tells an afflicted family that they must propitiate the spirit of their grandfather.

Stated briefly, it is the custom in traditional Shona society when the grandfather dies to name a bull after him. The animal may not be sold or disposed of, and after an interval, sometimes of several years, the spirit of the grandfather reclaims his bull. The spirit may reveal its wishes by causing a member of the family to fall ill, or by unsettling the bull so that it starts fighting with the other cattle, or wanders about looking lost and confused. Either of these events is enough to make the family visit a diviner who on this evidence, confirmed by the fall of the *hakata*, will tell his clients that the grandfather is demanding the meat of his bull.

During the early part of August 1961, I was fortunate enough to be invited to one of these ceremonies. Three Africans whom I knew well arrived at my house and asked me to accompany them on the following morning to their village where the bull dedicated to Madziwa, their grandfather, was to be sacrificed. I was delighted to accept the invitation as the ceremony is one that is seldom witnessed by Europeans.

[1] The Shona name for it is *Kutamba mudzimu*.

Offering to a spirit elder

I left at four o'clock in the morning and with the three Africans in my car drove about seventy miles outside Salisbury to the Mrewa reserve. It was quite light by the time we reached our destination, the village of Munjukuya. Some twenty minutes after our arrival, Chigodo, the seventy-year-old son of Madziwa, the deceased grandfather, led a procession of thirty men, mostly members of the family, to the cattle kraal to collect the bull.

The kraal, a circular enclosure with a fence of curved poles about four foot high, was only fifty yards away and the bull— a good-looking brown animal—was pointed out to me while everyone gathered round the fence nearest the spot where the bull was standing. Madziwa's son-in-law pointed a long spear at the bull while a grandson of Madziwa put on a black shawl, and prayed to his grandfather's spirit saying: 'Today you are to be given your *mombe*.'[1] The men clapped and the women shrilled loudly, though the few women who were present stood well away in the background.

The bull should then have been led out of the kraal to a *munhondo*[2] tree, about twenty yards nearer the village. This duty fell to the sons-in-law of Madziwa. One of them entered the kraal and successfully threw a long leather lasso over the horns of the beast and tightened the loop, but as the bull refused to move it was decided to move all the cattle, twenty or so animals, out of the kraal together. The bull followed the herd and was driven towards the *munhondo* tree and, as the bull reached it, another son-in-law picked up the end of the lasso and with the help of two other men forced the bull's neck against the trunk of the tree. A chain was put round the animal's head and held firmly so that its forehead stood out as an easy target. The oldest son-in-law now took up a huge hammer and brought it down between

[1] Cattle, but Africans used the same word in the singular for an ox, bull or cow.
[2] A deciduous tree, very common in this part of Africa, Julbernardia globiflora (Isoberlinia globiflora).

the bull's horns. The animal was stunned by the first blow and made unconscious by a further blow or two. The same man took a knife and proceeded to cut the bull's throat—a difficult task which required a fair amount of physical strength. A bowl was put beneath the slit throat and the blood was collected until three-quarters of the bowl was filled. Meanwhile, another son-in-law walked to another *munhondo* tree about fifty yards away and cut off some large leafy branches. He placed these alongside the bull's body, there were at least six large branches covering an area of about two square yards.

All these preliminaries, including the collecting of the correct amount of blood, took no more than twenty minutes. At this point, the wives of Chigodo and his brothers gathered together in a small group and sat down quietly to the right of the bull's head. A pot filled with water was handed to the principal wife who crawled on hands and knees to within a foot of the animal's head and, still kneeling, clapped her hands and said: '*Mashamba*', which means 'to wash'. She carefully, even tenderly, washed the forehead and face of the bull and then clapped her hands again. One of Chigodo's brothers then came up and completely covered the body of the bull with a black cloth.[1] All the men clapped and the women shrilled until a few minutes later the cloth was taken away.

The next part of the ceremony consisted in making the *rushanga*, or shrine. The sons-in-law cut four thin forked branches from the *munhondo* and the eldest one trimmed each branch to about a foot and a half in length leaving a six-inch fork at one end. Next he stripped the bark from each stick up to its forked end and tied the strips across the fork in a loose knot. Four small holes were dug in the ground about three feet apart, and one of the sticks was placed in each hole and the area round the sticks firmly closed up with soil. The shrine, in the form of a square, was close up to the trunk

[1] The *fuko* in which a dead person is wrapped.

Above, the senior son-in-law points his spear at the bull while the eldest son prays to the grandfather's spirit

Below left, the bull's head is tied to a tree

Below right, after the neck is opened the blood is collected in a basin

of the tree. The principal son-in-law now placed a small leafy branch off a *mushamba*[1] tree in the centre of the square.

As soon as the shrine was ready, the younger sons-in-law prepared a large fire some eight yards from the tree. While this was going on the eldest son-in-law, with two assistants, was busy skinning the body of the bull which was still lying on the branches of the *munhondo* tree. After the skinning, they removed the right forelimb, then the corresponding hind leg through its proximal joint. Next they opened the abdomen and removed about a pound of the omental fat; they did this by hand, without a knife, and placed the fat in the basin of blood. Some special pieces of meat—intended for the spirit of the grandfather—were then cut from the carcase, again by the principal son-in-law. This meat, called the *hwamu*, was cut from the inner side of each forelimb up to the pectoral region, and another piece, about the same size—two pounds—was cut from the flesh of the left loin; these pieces were placed on a wooden plate and a large slice of the liver was added and placed beside the *hwamu*. The chief son-in-law, assisted by one of his family, then began to cut each piece into long narrow strips, which were hung over the fire to roast. No salt was added.

While this meat was being roasted, the head of the bull was severed from the carcase through the joint at the neck and carried into the shrine. It was placed in the centre, its jaw on the ground and forehead and horns upright. A handful of dung removed from the intestines was placed on top of the forehead.

[1] Also deciduous (Lannea discolor).

Above, the carcase is covered with a black cloth while (*centre*) four sticks are placed round the foot of the tree to mark the shrine where (*below*) the head of the bull and a plate of the roasted meat are placed. The elder brother kneels to offer a last prayer to the grandfather's spirit.

The focus of interest then returned to the carcase where a four-inch piece of the small intestine, called *guru,* was cut and also a large slice of the liver. These were cut again into smaller pieces, about one and a half to two inches square, placed on a wooden plate, and every blood relation of the dead grandfather's family, male and female, child and adult, was given a piece of the raw meat to eat. I was interested to see how anxious the younger parents were that their children should eat a piece; if a child was too small or refused the meat, his father would rub it into his mouth. Within a few minutes, the roasted meat was ready and the long strips and the liver were also cut into smaller pieces about one to two inches square, placed on the wooden plate and handed over to Chigodo. He took the plate up to the edge of the shrine and placing it on the leaves, knelt down and clapped his hands while all the other men sat in a circle round the shrine. All clapped their hands together as Chigodo prayed: 'Grandfather, this is your roasted meat. Keep us well, including the European who is here.' After this brief prayer he ate a piece of the roasted meat, while each of the other participants also ate a piece. The main part of the ceremony was over, there only remained the *musiya*[1] which was then cooked on the fire and eaten.

The rest of the meat of the animal was cut up and cooked in pots by the women, who also made enough stiff porridge for everyone at the ceremony. When the food was ready three plates of meat with porridge were given to Chigodo, who placed them in the shrine. Men and women, all gathered round the tree. Chigodo took one of the plates and prayed to Madziwa's spirit, and informed him that this was the meat of his bull, cooked for all his children. He then took the second plate and prayed to Madziwa's father and after a further short prayer, took up the third plate of meat and porridge and offered it to the spirit of Madziwa's wife. This concluded

[1] The fat from the bull's stomach which had been placed in the basin of blood.

the prayers and the ceremony, and everyone was now free to eat and enjoy the food.

During the ceremony all the menial tasks such as killing and skinning the animal and preparing the shrine had been done by the sons-in-law of the dead Madziwa, and the important part—the prayers—were offered by his blood relations, the first by his grandson and the remainder by his eldest son, Chigodo.

CHAPTER 12

Pregnancy and the Shona midwife

Two conditions much dreaded by the Shona are sterility in a man and barrenness in a woman. The *nganga* have elaborate cures for both,[1] but once a cure has been effected in the case of a woman and she falls pregnant, the *nganga*, except for seeing her once during the ninth month of her pregnancy, leaves all the pre-natal care and the delivery of the baby to the Shona midwife.

Known in Mashonaland as *ambuya*[2], or *nyamukuta*, the midwife is usually an elderly, married woman with a reputation based on skill and experience. The methods these women use vary in detail from one district to another but the basic treatment and procedure is the same throughout the country.

A normal Shona girl, pregnant for the first time, waits until the fifth month when she first feels the baby move, before she and her husband visit the midwife. They take her a present, either a basket of grain, a fowl or a piece of meat. The husband tells her of his wife's condition and asks for a special medicine to 'open the door'. The midwife tells the woman how to cook this medicine with her mealie porridge and gives her a supply to take every day; she also arranges to visit her once a month until the eighth month.

[1] Appendix page 176.
[2] *Ambuya* is also the Shona name for grandmother; applied to the midwife it denotes age plus long experience of family life and is used by her clients as a form of endearment.

Each time she goes to their village the midwife examines the pregnant woman; she inserts her hand into the vagina, clenches her fist and then withdraws it. If she is unable to do this the passage is considered too narrow. This physical test and the special medicine to 'open the door' are vital parts of the midwife's treatment; the Mashona believe that without them the maternal passages will not widen sufficiently to allow a normal birth.

On the whole, little fault can be found with the midwife's method of handling a case during pregnancy. She does not interfere much with nature and her visits to the patient give the expectant mother confidence.

There are many taboos to be followed during pregnancy. A pregnant woman may not look at anything unpleasant; if, by chance, she sees something disagreeable she must not swallow her saliva until she has turned aside and spat out the bad sight; she must not eat the flesh of a tortoise or anything sour; she must not jump over a log or any firewood as this would delay the birth. She must not carry a winnowing basket on her head, for this might cause the infant's fontanelle to become too large or prevent it from closing at the normal age. She is not allowed to shake hands with anyone for fear that evil might be transferred through her to the child. Certain wild fruits are also forbidden her, and a woman who has become pregnant only after several years of marriage may not ford a stream.

The prospective mother works less than she would normally. In the case of a first pregnancy, a message is sent to her mother in the sixth month and shortly afterwards she is escorted to her parents' home by one of her husband's sisters. She stays with them until after the baby is born, though in subsequent pregnancies she remains in her husband's village as she is expected to have sufficient experience to manage without her mother's help and encouragement.

The midwife is summoned as soon as labour starts. But before she embarks on her duties she has to drink a special medicine[1] to prevent her eyes from being damaged when she looks at the exposed genitalia of the mother. It is generally feared by the Mashona that if a man or a woman looks at the genitalia of another, whether of the same sex or not, that that person will become blind.[2] The midwife also has to wash her face and hands in another medicine before she is ready to help with the labour.

The patient's mother is always present at this time, usually her grandmother, and her mother-in-law too, if she can leave her own family to be there. They help the midwife, but the real importance of their presence is to act as witnesses to the birth—an essential formality in Mashonaland. When the baby arrives, these women shrill to let the rest of the village know that the mother has been successfully delivered, they shrill once for a girl and twice for a boy.

Normal labour is, in certain respects, well-conducted, since there is no interference in its course. In some cases the midwife rubs the entrance to the vagina with a soapy mixture of herbs[3] to facilitate delivery. In the first stage of labour the woman walks about the hut or sits on the floor, but in the second stage with its abdominal contractions, she is given some help. Completely naked, she sits on a mat on the floor with her back supported by the grinding mortar (found in every Shona home) or by rolled-up blankets. Her knees are flexed and parted and she is instructed to grip the back of each knee and thigh as she presses downwards. To give additional support to her back, her mother, or one of the other women, kneels or stands behind her with forearms under the patient's arms, pulling upwards while she pushes in the opposite direction. The midwife kneels in front ready to receive the baby. Unfortunately nothing is

[1] Prepared from the roots of the *chifumuro* and *muchingazuva* trees.
[2] A man who stares at a naked woman is said to develop *showera*, a disease characterized by lumps forming on the eyelids.
[3] Crushed roots of the *musirika*, *nyabahuro* and *chisukavakadzi* are soaked in water and the extract is mixed with *mufuta* oil.

done about the mother's bowels and bladder, and she is allowed to eat if she wishes during labour.

When the baby is delivered, the cord is not cut until the placenta has been expelled. If, after a few hours, it is still retained, the midwife may be tempted to pull on the cord, or she may insert her hand and remove the placenta manually. The cord is then severed with a sharp piece of reed, or more often today, with a razor blade, and the placenta is buried in the hut. If the site of the cut bleeds, the midwife applies a little herbal ointment—a practice which makes it easy to understand why septic cords and tetanus of the new-born are so prevalent in Africa. It is not customary to bathe a Shona baby when it is born, instead the midwife usually rubs it all over with castor oil.

The husband is told as soon as his wife is delivered, and through him, the father-in-law. The new mother is not allowed to leave the hut, except to attend to her natural functions, until about six days after the birth. Traditionally, the husband may not see his child or enter the hut until the cord has separated, nor may the floor of the hut be swept or cleaned until then. Usually the cord separates about the fifth day and the midwife sweeps the hut and smears the floor with fresh manure.

Soon after this event, an interesting ritual used to take place whereby the baby was named. Although it is seldom practised today, the rite is worth recording. The midwife rubbed two sticks together and started a fire in the middle of the hut. On it she cooked the flesh of a goat which the husband had previously killed. She mixed the meat with medicinal herbs, and then invited in the women of the neighbourhood to eat a share. After the meal she filled a small clay pot with water and asked the mother what name she would like to give the baby. Holding the child in the palm of her hand, she pronounced the name, and afterwards bathed the baby for the first time since its birth in the water from the pot. The father was now told the name of his child and informed that he might return to his home.

It is about this time that the midwife places a charm or a little medicine, wrapped in a piece of cotton material, on a string round the baby's neck to facilitate the closure of the fontanelle. Shona parents believe that this is the weakest and most vulnerable part of a baby's body and one of the midwife's first actions after a birth is to make sure that the fontanelle is normal. She measures with her little finger the distance from the bridge of the baby's nose to the beginning of the anterior fontanelle. She also measures the width of the fontanelle itself, more than three fingers in breadth is considered abnormal and a sign that the baby will sooner or later lose weight, or develop diarrhoea, a cough, or a high fever. It is then that every precaution is taken—from providing the baby with extra charms to coating the area with a special tarry substance—to ensure that this potentially weak spot is adequately protected.

After the birth of her first baby, the woman remains in her parents' home for about four weeks, by then it is time for the baby to be shown to the people of her husband's village. She spends the first few days after her return in her father-in-law's hut, only moving into her own after all the villagers have been to see the baby and brought presents.

When the baby is in its fifth month the parents are expected to pay the midwife. Taking the baby with them, they set off to see her with a small basket of fine meal and a fowl or some meat.[1] Until this visit is made, the husband and wife are not permitted sexual intercourse.

So far we have only described a pregnancy that ends well with a live baby. If the labour is slow or becomes obstructed, other, and often dangerous, rituals are carried out. If labour lasts for longer than forty-eight hours, the Mashona believe,

[1] There is little variation between the midwife's fees and the presents which the family give her when they first go and see her.

like members of most other African tribes, that the woman must have been unfaithful to her husband, and that in order for her labour to become normal she must confess. The midwife asks her if she has been unfaithful, and if she says 'yes' the matter is reported to her husband and the guilty man is later fined. If she protests that she is innocent and there is still no progress in the labour, the older women become desperate and try to force a confession by putting her through an ordeal. A thin switch or a narrow strip of leather dried with salt is bound round her head or wrist, when tightened it becomes so painful that it is guaranteed to elicit a confession. If the labour is still delayed after the confession, or if the woman persists in her denials, recourse is made to a diviner, and the *hakata* decide whether or not she is innocent. All this involves delay, a factor which is often advantageous in labour and more often than not the contractions increase normally and the pregnancy terminates well. On the other hand, in cases of serious obstruction, these delays cause the uterus to rupture; this unfortunately happens more often in Africa today than in any other part of the world.

A woman who has been delivered of a baby and who had been considered barren until treated by a *nganga*, has one more duty to perform. When her baby begins to walk she kills a hen if it is a girl, or a cock in the case of a boy, as a thank-offering to the *nganga* whom she and her husband invite to their village. After they have eaten the meat they take the child to an anthill where the *nganga* crushes some roots[1] and puts them in a pot of water. He dips his badge of office—the ritual tail—into the water and sprinkles the child four times. The Shona believe that unless this ceremony is carried out at the right time the child will become ill or grow up mentally retarded.

A *nganga*'s fee for curing a barren woman is £5. This

---

[1] *Chifumuro* (Dicoma anomala), *gundamiti*, *mupingagona* and *mutara* (Gardenia resiniflua).

sounds exorbitant compared to his usual fees and in relation to the Shona's usual earning capacity, but one has to remember the overriding concern of the African to have children. Apart from his deep and genuine love of them, they confer status and after he dies this status is transferred with him to the world of spirits.

CHAPTER 13

Preventive medicine and charms

prevention-control

A large part of the *nganga*'s practice is concerned with prescribing preventive remedies, for his patients believe that he can confer immunity against specific types of illnesses. The Shona's faith in his doctor goes much further than the European's in this respect because he believes that the *nganga* can also prescribe medicine which will protect him against misfortune and from here it is only a very short step to his belief in the *nganga*'s capacity to confer positive benefits such as outstanding physical strength, attraction to the opposite sex and other desirable qualities which we have already examined in the *nganga*'s repertoire of sympathetic magic.

Preventive medicines are dispensed either in the form of medicine or of charms. The best way to understand how and why these are prescribed is to examine the care lavished on a new-born baby.

The Shona parent knows that a baby succumbs much more easily to disease than an adult, and in common with all other tribal Africans, he is very conscious of the high infant mortality rate. As soon as a healthy baby is born, therefore, the main concern of the father and mother is to ensure that it keeps well. The father sends a message to the *nganga* to inform him of his wife's successful delivery, and after the *nganga* has received confirmation from the midwife he arrives with his medicine to protect the new baby. He soaks five different roots in water, and as each root has a different property I have listed them by their Shona names:

1. The *zuva* root—to guard against general weakness.
2. The *nkova* root—to prevent the head from becoming too large.
3. The *chikosoro* root—to prevent coughing.
4. The *ndongorongo* root—to prevent an illness characterized by vomiting and abdominal pains round the umbilicus.
5. The *nyashungu* root—to prevent the umbilicus from becoming larger.

Twice a day—in the morning and at midday—the child is bathed in the water in which the roots have soaked. After six days, if the child is strong and healthy, the roots are thrown on to the ashheap, but if the baby is ailing the herbal baths are continued for another two months.

When the child is about six months old, or just beginning to crawl, the *nganga* prescribes a medicine[1] to prevent convulsions. This is also added to the water in which the baby is washed and the treatment is continued for three weeks. A little later, about the time the child is beginning to walk, the *nganga* prepares a medicine[2] to ensure good and healthy dentition. The mother rubs it on the child's teeth and gums three times a day for a week.

Another early treatment recommended by the *nganga* is a medicine called *ndongorongo*, made from roots,[3] which prevents diarrhoea and pains in the umbilical region. He usually gives the roots to the midwife and she passes them on to the mother who chews them and spits the medicine directly into the baby's mouth. She does this twice a day for three days, beginning shortly after the birth.

Also very popular is a medicine used to rub on the fon-

---

[1] Called *mushongwa webuka*, it is made by crushing the roots of *nyazema, muchingazura,* and *muhora*.
[2] From the root of the *gariro*.
[3] Roots of the *ndongorongo* and *nyashungu*.

tanelle and hasten its closure. The *nganga* burns a root[1] to charcoal and mixes it with peanut oil.[2] He dips his little finger into this tarry preparation and smears it along the soft sutures leading to the fontanelle, starting at the forehead and continuing backwards until the fontanelle itself is covered; as we have seen the Shona believes that this is the weakest spot in the baby's body and that illness and evil enter this way. The belief is no doubt strengthened by the mother noticing when her baby is ill—from gastro-enteritis, vomiting or broncho-pneumonia—that the pulsations of the fontanelle are weaker than usual. She will often, on her own initiative, procure some tarry material and smear it over the fontanelle as a protective layer to prevent any more harm from penetrating.

Nganga also prescribe medicine to protect a child from being bewitched. One *nganga* I know prescribes this medicine when the child is old enough for its first haircut, usually between two and four years old. It is a fairly complicated medicine to make up, consisting of three kinds of roots[3] which are crushed to a fine powder and mixed with the fruit of a fourth tree[4] and the root and bark of a fifth.[5] *Mafuta*, or castor oil, is added and the mixture is smeared over the child's body, morning and evening, for two months.

After the child is seven years old, he receives the same medical attention as an adult and no more special preventive medicines are given. But before, and after, he reaches this age he will wear a variety of charms all bearing a different or protective attribute.

As soon as her baby is born, the Shona mother is busy procuring charms. She will probably hang the first one round its neck before it is a week old. Sometimes it is given to her by a friend, or it may be one that she already has, or

---

[1] The *chirambadziva* root.
[2] *Nzungu.*
[3] *Mutara, mutandika* and *mbanda.*
[4] *Mafuta* tree—from which the castor oil seed is gathered.
[5] *Muteyo* tree.

has bought from a *nganga*. Most of the charms worn by infants are intended to counteract evil spells in case they have the misfortune to be touched by a strange woman who may be a witch. At least thirty per cent of babies admitted to my wards wear this kind of charm—usually threaded on a string round the babies' necks or waists.

Often a baby wears more than one charm, the number and types depending on the parents' special fears for their child. Each charm has its own significance; one may be intended as a protection against diarrhoea, another against a cough, a third to prevent loss of weight. A popular one, supposed to ensure the proper and timely closure of the fontanelle is known as *chipande*. It consists of a small circular portion of bone cut from the occipital area of a baboon's or sheep's skull. A piece of string is threaded through a small hole pierced in the centre and this bone disc is hung round the baby's neck. It is not usually worn until the placental cord has separated, about five to ten days after birth. This charm falls into the category of sympathetic magic, because of the inference that the soft fontanelle will become as hard and tough as the skull of a baboon or sheep.

A universal fear among Shona mothers is that if a baby is touched by a menstruating or pregnant woman, it may become dangerously ill, because a woman in either condition is considered unclean and harmful to others. To guard against this eventuality, a mother cuts off a piece of root from the *chifumuro* bush, about half an inch to an inch long, pierces a hole through it and hangs this amulet round the baby's neck. This root is also worn by adults as a charm to prevent evil influences from entering their bodies.

Shona parents believe that a witch wishing harm to their child will introduce a red shell[1] into the hut where the family sleep. Suspicion that a witch has been successful in doing this is confirmed if the child falls sick and instead of respond-

[1] *Nyengeredzi*. I have asked various *nganga* the meaning of the red shell but they have not been able to tell me.

ing to the *nganga*'s treatment continues to worsen and lose weight, (continued vomiting in a sick child, on the other hand, would indicate the activity of an ancestral spirit). To counteract the witch's spell, the *nganga* orders a small white shell to be put in the baby's bath water once a month at the time of the new moon, and a larger one twice a week. The mother does this for six months and believes that this will also protect her child if it is touched by a pregnant or menstruating woman.

Also intended to prevent a child from being harmed by a witch is a charm called *mbinjiri*. It is made of two pairs of small cylindrical-shaped pieces of wood[1] which are tied round the waist—one pair hangs in front and the other over the sacrum. Sometimes another charm called *zango*[2] is added to the *mbinjiri* charm and placed between the two sticks. It is worn to prevent the child, while still at the breast, from becoming ill should its parents have sexual intercourse, the resulting illness being known as *kupwera* or *kutangira*.

Charms are by no means restricted to babies or small children. There is a brisk trade in their sale for adults. They are bought for a variety of purposes—to succeed in games, to retain the love of a husband or wife, to find work, to win the approbation of an employer or friends, to gain a lover, in fact there is hardly an eventuality for which a charm cannot be procured. Ointments too are purchased, and are believed to have the same properties as charms. They are rubbed into the skin or into incisions cut in the body; for instance, I have often seen incisions cut over the knuckles of Shona boxers, and the ointment rubbed into them is supposed to enable them to punch very hard.

Nganga, as well as their patients, possess charms for their own personal use. A *nganga* once stayed in my house, and

---

[1] From the roots of the *munungwara* tree, though there are two other types of *mbinjiri* charms, one made from the *muhururu* tree and the other from the red seeds of the *mutiti* tree.

[2] From the roots of the *cheredzawaba*.

during his visit I saw that he had a charm in his room. He told me that it was to help him with his driving test which he was very anxious to pass.

One of the most common charms in Mashonaland is called *zango*. It has a variety of components including a small piece of root which is wrapped in a piece of cloth together with various small objects, such as pieces of skin, stones and feathers. The edges of the cloth are stitched firmly round the contents and the finished article is attached to a string. The colour of the cloth varies, it may be red, blue or white, and the *zango*, shaped like a ring or a lifebuoy, is worn round the arm by adults and round the waist by children. It is a multi-purpose charm and is worn as a protection against witches, to confer good fortune in love or gambling, to prevent illness and for many other reasons.

Some Mashona men carry special roots on their persons to prevent accidents, particularly when they are about to take their driving tests. Others wear charms to protect themselves against attack by snakes or wild animals.

There is a curious charm called *mbinjiri*[1] which is worn by women who wish to prevent pregnancy. It is made up of pairs of small cylindrical roots, each about half an inch in length. A small hole is pierced through each so that they can be strung around the waist and usually three pairs are worn at the same time. The Shona believes very strongly in the efficacy of this charm and though it is difficult to understand why it should work, perhaps the strong suggestive influence operates in the same way as a European woman's fear that she will not conceive.

Besides the charms worn by individuals and babies, there is also a charm which protects the entire family. It consists of an animal's horn filled with powdered medicines and is hidden in the hut to protect the family from witchcraft.

A Shona woman usually attaches her charms to the string

[1] Made from the roots of the *mbinjiri* tree (Cassia singueana).

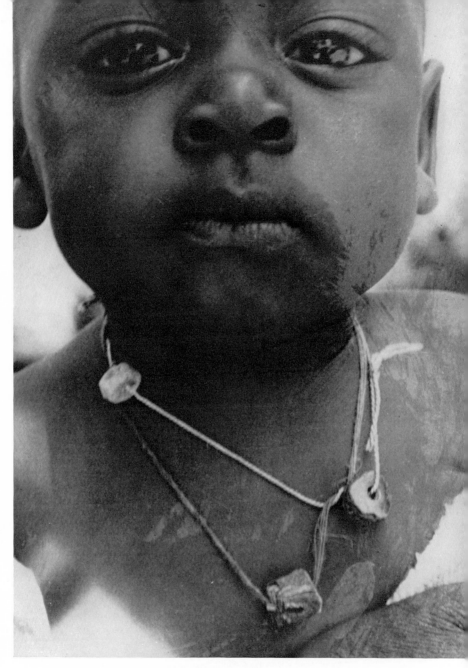

Three charms often seen on children: the one on the left is made of bone and is believed to hasten the closure of the fontanelle

Zango charms are worn round the neck by this woman to ensure good health and as a protection against evil; she wears a third charm on her arm

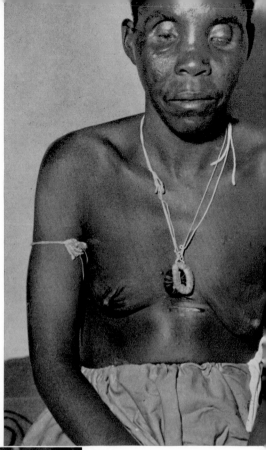

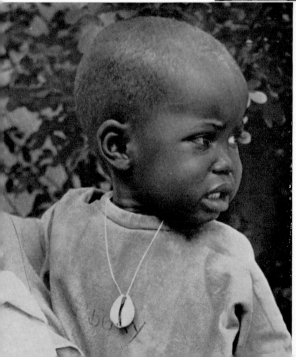

A shell is sometimes used as a charm to prevent illness

of beads she wears round her waist, while a man may either carry his in his pocket or wear them on his arm. The important point is that they should be worn on unexposed parts of the body. This rule does not apply to babies or small children, but if charms worn by adults are seen by other people, they are said to lose their efficacy.

CHAPTER 14

Shona medicine and Western medicine

I have never encountered any hostility in the *nganga*'s attitude to me as a doctor nor, indeed, to the practice of Western medicine as a whole. No doubt this is because the African, knowing that the European has introduced science and technology to his country, credits him with an equivalent skill in medicine. But even with the advent of the first white man to Central Africa this confidence existed. The journals of David Livingstone and Robert Moffat are full of references to the countless Africans who flocked to them for medicines, and the white missionaries and doctors who followed the early explorers all reported the same phenomenon. Perhaps this eagerness is explained by the Africans' love of medicine for itself, because they saw no contradiction in taking the 'new medicine' and continuing to be treated by their *nganga*.

The *nganga*'s belief in the efficacy of Western medicine is very evident in the many talks I have had with them, and is true of both herbalists and diviners. It is supported too by the fact that *nganga* frequently visit me to discuss their patients and illnesses and by the fact that they are quite happy to send difficult cases to a European hospital. Opposition, where it exists, is much more likely to come from the *nganga*'s patients.

The Mashona believe very strongly in the efficacy of their medical culture, in its wisdom and virtue and in the countless medical secrets which have been handed down from one generation to another through the family *nganga* spirits. One also has to remember that their faith in the *nganga* is tied up to a large extent with their religious beliefs. It is therefore not surprising that they feel that their *nganga*—heirs to this great medical and spiritual knowledge—are the only doctors who can understand what is wrong when they are ill and so cure them. Their reluctance to consult a European doctor is not that they doubt the European's skill as a doctor but that they are inclined to apply the same principle to him as they do to their own *nganga*, and believe that his skill is more likely to be effective on Europeans than on themselves. The African is also convinced that some diseases attack only the black man and in these cases, they argue, it would be quite useless to expect a European to cure them.

Because of this attitude, many of the more traditional and conservative Mashona prefer to live and die under the ministrations of the *nganga*. But this, I must emphasize, is a question of choice and not of taboos. The only traditional Africans I know who categorically refuse to be treated by Western medicine are the *mhondoro*—the mediums of the tribal spirits. Their objection is purely religious and has nothing to do with colour, as the taboo would apply equally if the Western-trained doctor were an African. Tribal law strictly forbids them to seek aid from any but their own *nganga*.

The more progressive, or urban Shona will go to a European doctor if the *nganga* fails to cure him. The majority of my Shona patients come to me in this way; equally, if I fail to cure them (and there are many disorders I must admit to little success in alleviating), my patients ask to leave hospital to consult their *nganga*. As a result, there is today a constant flow of African patients between the doctors of both civilizations. It is not only confined to patients—very often the *nganga* come to consult me about their own ailments.

Conceding to the *nganga* the professional status which he undoubtedly holds in his own community, it is interesting to compare some of his ethics with those of his Western colleagues.

A definite, if unwritten, code exists as to what a *nganga* may or may not do. For instance, no *nganga* may advertise or promote his own competence, nor may he discuss his qualifications with strangers. His reputation stands or falls on the success of his treatments. A *nganga* may not criticize or find fault with other *nganga*; I can substantiate this claim as I have never heard one criticizing the methods of another.

No action can be taken against a *nganga* who is negligent or who is believed responsible for the death or deterioration in health of a patient. Even if an individual or a family feel that they have grounds for accusing a *nganga* of malpractice they may not report him to the chief. Retribution is believed to follow in the normal course of events as such a *nganga* will develop a bad reputation and his practice will fall off. Similarly, a family has no redress if a *nganga* refuses to treat one of its members, or if he decides to stop treatment in the middle of a course of therapy, which he might well do if he found out that the family were not carrying out his instructions.

On his side, the patient may leave his *nganga* if he is dissatisfied with his treatment. He need give no warning or explanation and the next *nganga* he consults is not obliged to inform the first one that his patient has come to him. The *nganga* cannot sue the patient any more than the patient can sue him. Nor can the *nganga* appeal to the chief to recover what is owing if his fees are not paid because the debt is considered a purely private matter between him and his patient. Incidentally, I have never heard a Shona complain that the fees charged by his *nganga* were too high.

The *nganga* cannot belong to any union or association because divining and methods of treatment are considered the property of each individual *nganga*. As his skill and knowledge have been given to him by his healing spirit, it is believed that the spirit would be very displeased if he were to share his secrets with other *nganga*. So each works independently, jealously guarding his knowledge and experience.

But though the traditional *nganga* operates in this way, there has been an attempt recently among *nganga* practising in the urban areas of Southern Rhodesia to form themselves into an association. Most of them are herbalists, they neither divine themselves nor—as orthodox procedure demands—do they advise their clients first to seek a diviner to find out the spiritual cause of their illnesses. They are, in fact, nothing more than pharmacists who prescribe and sell herbs and charms over the counter. They even buy many of their herbs from other *nganga*, instead of looking for them themselves, and also unlike the traditional herbalist, they charge for every herb they prescribe instead of waiting to collect their fees after a cure has been effected and the client's family is satisfied. Though the group is now established it is not receiving the support of the traditional *nganga*.

It is not easy to know how much rivalry there is between *nganga*[1]. I am told by the Mashona that it exists, but I have not come across it myself. There are fewer opportunities for professional jealousy than in Western medical practice, because except for the period of apprenticeship, *nganga* work independently, and with no team work and no hospitals it is difficult for one *nganga* to know of another's success. But though they do not collaborate over a case, they are perfectly willing to send their patients on to another *nganga* if their patients want a second opinion. An interesting rule amongst herbalists lays down that if a patient has been treated for twenty-one days and shows no sign of improvement, the *nganga* withdraws from the case and advises his patient to seek another opinion. Medically, this custom is a good one as it tends to discourage over-treatment and it also

[1] Professor Evans-Pritchard (op. cit. p. 203) found a lot of jealousy amongst the Azande doctors in the Sudan.

gives the patient an opportunity of changing his doctor without hurting his feelings.

Another difference between the *nganga* and the Western doctor is that the *nganga*, owning his own plot of land which he can develop and live off, is not dependant on his medical fees, although of course they add, sometimes quite considerably, to his comforts and standard of living. This economic independence prevents him from being over-concerned about the payment of his fees.

The *nganga*, like any other doctor, has to weigh his advice carefully and consider the consequences of his treatment. If he acts precipitously or is negligent he will lose his reputation and his practice. But besides his medical deportment, equal emphasis is placed on his behaviour as a human being. He must conduct himself in a respectable manner and be kind and helpful to everyone, regardless of their status, because he is there to help the whole community. The Shona believes that if a *nganga* behaves in a shameful or unsatisfactory way, his healing spirit, whether it is a *mudzimu* or a *shave*, will leave him. That is why if a *nganga* were to boast about his knowledge or ability, he would not only be considered an unlikeable person but his medical reputation would become suspect.

The patient-doctor relationship is a strong one between the *nganga* and the Shona; based on esteem it includes great affection as well. With his sympathy and understanding, the *nganga* is as great a friend to his patients as the European family practitioner is to his. A proof of this is that hardly a week passes without one of my hospital patients, or his relations, asking us to allow him out to see his *nganga*.

And now what about the attitude of the European doctor to the *nganga*? The unscientific approach of the *nganga* prevents the Western doctor from taking his claim of 'doctor' seriously. As a result the strength of the *nganga*-patient relationship is often underestimated and there is a lack of informed interest about his practice. I think this is unfortunate for several reasons, perhaps the most important is that the European doctor is apt to discount the *nganga*'s superiority in psychological therapy, for there can be no doubt that in cases which respond to suggestion the *nganga*, invested with the absolute confidence of his patients, is very successful indeed. This confidence, or reassurance, plays a very important part in the African's recovery when he is being treated in a European hospital, even if his illness is one which responds easily to clinical treatment. Unfortunately, reassurance can only be given by those in whom confidence has been placed.

Obviously the Western doctor starts at a disadvantage here. He cannot compete with the superb stage craft of the *nganga*—the regalia, incantations and ritual which help to create confidence in his ability. The rather ordinary appearance of the European doctor is bound to compare unfavourably with the aura of power and wisdom surrounding the *nganga*.

But where I feel the Western doctor *should* compete in winning the confidence of his African patients is through a better understanding of their background; too often—because of language difficulties and pressure of work—he is unable either to show a sufficient interest in personal problems, or to assess their importance against the environment, village community life, religion, customs, superstitions, and fears of his patients. Only within this context can the problems and worries of an individual patient be related to his physical complaints. Unless an African patient is approached with sufficient understanding to make the relationship with his doctor a friendly and sympathetic one, the scientific doctor will be unable to gain his confidence and as a result will often be unable to cure him, and the Shona instead of being won over to Western medicine will continue to rely on his *nganga*.

Having stated the case for the good *nganga* to the best of my ability, and based it on my experience and knowledge of the Shona *nganga*, one must inevitably face up to the question: what is the future of the 'witch doctor' in Africa? There can be only one answer—there is no place for him. Because in spite of his many qualities the *nganga* is today the greatest single obstacle to a more enlightened way of life and to the African's progress in civilization.

As a doctor, he can be credited with the discovery of herbal remedies some of which may, when their properties have been investigated, prove of lasting benefit to mankind, and he can be credited too with an ability to treat simple psychological disturbances by suggestion, but these contributions are heavily outweighed by the delay caused through patients consulting him at a stage when their illnesses might be treated effectively with drugs or surgery. Medically, therefore, his presence is a handicap.

But more retrogressive, and infinitely more important, is his position as the fountain-head of African belief in good and evil spirits. One may argue that a society which believed that acts of meanness and envy, amoral or asocial ways of life, are manifestations of a witch, and which therefore condones the victimisation of the wrongdoer, makes for good behaviour inside that society, but those who know the African and his fears engendered by witchcraft will feel that good behaviour can be achieved at too great a price.

The *nganga* is the hub round which the spiritual world revolves, and so long as he functions as a dispenser of antidotes to witchcraft, so long will the African's bondage to fear continue.

PART II

Practical and Field Observations

CHAPTER I

Interviews with nganga

I recently questioned ten *nganga* from different parts of the country in order to find out how each had qualified. Six of the *nganga* I visited were men and four were women. I record here the results of my investigations as they illustrate the different ways in which each first became aware of his medical calling.

1. CHIRUMA: a woman aged about forty-five, practises in the Chiduku reserve some eighty miles from Salisbury. Her aunt had been a *nganga*. She was already married when she began to dream about medicines. A few years later she fell ill. Her husband consulted a diviner and was told that her aunt's *mudzimu* wanted Chiruma to succeed her as a *nganga*. Chiruma's parents would not accept this opinion and went to another *nganga*, who confirmed what the first had said. He advised them to brew beer and to hold a ceremony at which they were to inform the aunt's spirit that Chiruma was willing to be a *nganga*. This they did and after the ceremony she recovered from her illness and went to work with her mother-in-law who was also a *nganga*. She taught Chiruma the various procedures and also instructed her about herbal remedies. After this apprenticeship, Chiruma was accepted as a fully-fledged *nganga*. She is able to divine as well as to treat with herbs; in common with all women *nganga*, she divines without *hakata* and when possessed by her healing spirit she communicates to

her clients through her husband who acts as her assistant and interprets what the spirit has said.

2. MAKUBABA: about sixty years of age and comes from the Devedzo district. He is said to be a specialist in divining the cause of death and uses *hakata*; he is also a herbalist. His father was a very celebrated *nganga* and several of his relations were so keen to inherit his healing spirit that they arranged with a *nganga* to carry out an ordeal while he was still alive to find out which member of the family would inherit it. The ordeal was performed by a *nganga* called Masendi, and Makubaba was the only one who vomited the medicine given to members of the family: a sign which confirmed that the spirit would select him when his father died. In the meantime Makubaba helped his father, who took him on his rounds, and by the time the old man died, two years ago, he knew a great deal about his practice. After his father's death he began to dream frequently about herbs. Although he is now about sixty years old, he is not fully qualified and is still attached to a qualified *nganga*. He waits to learn either in a dream, or through another *nganga*, when he can hold the ceremony which will end his apprenticeship and allow him to set up on his own. Whenever he is consulted by a patient, he divines with his *hakata* to find out whether the medicine he prescribes is likely to be effective. If the answer is unsatisfactory, he advises the patient to go to another *nganga*.

3. TAMBADZAI: a woman aged forty-five, comes from the Newedzi reserve and specializes in "sucking out" illnesses[1] and treating barren women. Her aunt was a herbalist and after she died Tambadzai became ill. A diviner was consulted and told Tambadzai that her illness was caused by her aunt whose healing spirit wanted to possess her so that she could carry on with her work. He advised her to hold a

[1] Treatment known in Shona as *kupumha*.

ceremony for her aunt's *shave*. It was at this time that she began to dream about cures. Tambadzai was already married, but had no children, and the diviner also told her that after she had held the ceremony she would have children, but if she did not accept the *shave* she would remain childless. After the ceremony had taken place she became pregnant and has since had other children. Her apprenticeship to another *nganga*, from whom she learnt much, ended with a ceremony to which several other *nganga* were invited, and thus she became a fully-fledged *nganga*.

4. MURAPI: about thirty-eight years old, speaks fluent English and is employed by a large company in Salisbury. He comes from the Chiweshe reserve and was educated at a mission school. When he left school, he was a Christian and lived according to the Christian faith. His grandfather's sister was a *nganga* with a fine reputation in the district, and after her death one of the children in the family became ill. A *nganga* was sought and he told the family that the *mudzimu* of the deceased wished Murapi to take over her art of healing. But Murapi, who was then in his early twenties, refused to accept this opinion because of his Christian beliefs. Other members of the family became ill, and other *nganga* were consulted, each one giving the same reason for the illnesses in the family and insisting that Murapi should practise medicine. Finally he was impressed by the same pronouncement coming from so many different sources and agreed to follow in the footsteps of his great-aunt. He gave up Christianity and began to practise as a herbalist in the Chinamora reserve; he had been instructed by his great-aunt when he was still a child and so had the advantage of knowing many of her herbal remedies. During the week he works as an ordinary employee in Salisbury and at weekends practises medicine in the reserve.

5. RAZI: A Shona-speaking *nganga* from Chifunga, Razi

belongs to the Muchangani tribe. He is about forty-six years old and a very fit African. In 1944, when he was about thirty, he returned from Johannesburg where he had been working, and joined his father who was practising as a *nganga* in the Chifunga district. His father taught him how to read the *hakata,* and he also used to send him to the veld to collect plants and showed him how to prepare them and how to treat sick people who were not able to visit his father. After two years his father died and Razi carried on his practice. A year later he held a ceremony, which was attended by elders of the villages as well as another *nganga,* and Razi prayed to his father's *mudzimu* to help and guide him in his work. After he had been in practice for five years, his father appeared to him in a dream and told him not to charge his patients before they were treated, but only after they had been cured. Until then Razi had been charging five shillings before each herbal treatment, but after the dream he stopped this practice and has never done it since. Razi is considered specially skilled in treating sterility in the male and female, abdominal pains in pregnancy and pains over the heart; he practises as a diviner as well as a herbalist and he charges a fee of £1 for a cure. The way in which he qualified differs from that of most other *nganga* questioned in that he neither became ill nor suffered any mental upset. He holds the usual annual ceremony for his father's *mudzimu* at which beer is prepared and a goat killed.

6. JACOB MAKOREARATA: aged forty-five, Jacob Makorearata, has been in practice in the Harare township of Salisbury for the past nine years. Previously he lived in the Kandeya reserve of the Mount Darwin district. When he was about twenty-seven and already married, he began to suffer from pains in his body and indigestion and began to lose weight; he also admits that during this illness he went off his head. At times, he was found outside his room and had no idea how he had got there. He was ill for two

years before his father decided to consult a diviner, who told him that the illness was caused by the spirit of his mother's dead father, who had been a *nganga* and wanted Jacob to become one. Beer was prepared and a ceremony held, and after this he recovered and began to dream about where he should dig for his medicines. His first dream told him how to cure a swollen abdomen, and his second how to treat pneumonia by making incisions on the chest wall; he also learnt which medicines should be given by mouth. In another dream he learnt that in order to treat headaches he should dig up a certain root, scrape off the dirt and give it to the patient to smell until the tears streamed from his eyes. Further dreams taught him how to cure diarrhoea with blood and how to handle a case of scabies; these dreams continue to guide his practice today. After five years he was publicly recognized as a *nganga* and held a ceremony for his *shave*, at which he was accepted by the people. He was not taught by another *nganga*; and the only help and guidance he ever received was through dreams which he attributed to the *shave* spirit of his grandfather, which was of the *bveni*[1] type. Jacob is strictly a herbalist and does no divining.

7. WHASAI: forty-five years old and practises in the Chiweshe reserve. When he was about twenty-nine he became ill and for five years complained of shortness of breath, chest pain, swelling of the legs, weakness of the body and mental confusion. None of his relations or ancestors had been a *nganga*. His father visited a diviner and was told that Whasai's illness was due to a healing *shave* that wished to be accepted by him. Beer was prepared and at the ceremony a *shave* called Mukombwe, who apparently originated from a strange country, entered Whasai and said: 'I am the one who caused the illness and I want you to help other

---

[1] Baboon—the Shona do not know why possession by a baboon spirit should convey healing talents, all other healing *mashave* originate from man.

people as a *nganga*.' Whasai recovered after the ceremony, and patients started coming to him for help. His father acted as his assistant and recorded what was said when Whasai divined and treated while possessed by the *shave*. A year after the first ceremony, a larger one was held for the *shave* at which Whasai was publicly accepted as a *nganga*. He never dreamed about remedies nor did he attach himself to other doctors for instruction; he practises as a herbalist as well as divining with *hakata*. He is consulted about the cause of death.

8. JEXA: a woman of about forty, born in the Chiota reserve. Her grandfather had been a *nganga* and when she was thirty-seven his spirit began to trouble her. She developed a nervous disorder which made her unable to straighten her arms and legs; she also complained of a stiff neck and, although unable to close her eyes, she could not see. After two months a *nganga* was consulted, and the family learnt that the grandfather wished Jexa to continue his medical work. They were advised to brew beer and pray to his *mudzimu*. At the ceremony Jexa became possessed and her spirit told the people who were gathered there what clothes it wanted its host to wear. After the ceremony she began to practise and was able to divine; she also started to dream about herbal medicines and went to the woods to dig for the roots she had dreamt about. She does not use *hakata* but divines during possession by her spirit.

9. JAVANEKA: an adult female *nganga* of the Makorekore tribe, born in the Chiota reserve at the village where Nyandoro, her grandmother, practised as a doctor. Her grandmother had a Shangano healing *shave*; she brought up her granddaughter and taught her how to treat patients. After her death, when Javaneka was already married and had a child, she became ill with mental confusion and also had attacks of shivering and vomiting. She was sick for a year

before her parents consulted a *nganga*, who told them that their daughter's condition was due to her grandmother's Shangano *shave* wishing to enter her. If she wished to recover, she must accept the spirit at a special ceremony. Beer was prepared and she became possessed at the ceremony. She could not remember what the spirit said, but her family assured her that it was her grandmother's *shave* and that she could now treat patients. The spirit would help her to make barren women have children and to cure the disease of *ndongorongo*[1] in babies, and also oedema of the legs and arms, headaches, epistaxis, and varicose veins.

Javaneka made a full recovery after the ceremony and has been practising for twenty years. Throughout this period she has dreamed about herbal remedies and where to find the herbs. She told me that she sometimes also dreams of the complaint and its remedy before the patient comes to consult her. She practises as a herbalist and does not divine. Twice a year she holds a ceremony to thank the *shave* for helping her to practise successfully.

10. JOEL: another Makorekore, is twenty-eight years old and was born in the Wedza reserve. When he was eighteen and in the Standard VI class at St Mark's Primary School in the Mhondoro reserve, he started feeling ill every evening at the same time—about 6.30—and became mentally confused. He also became dizzy and curious things happened just as he was about to fall asleep—he used to feel as if he were fighting with other people, or he saw himself climbing mountains, or trying to catch the sun or fighting two lions. After fighting the lions he would suddenly be restored to his normal self and find himself in bed. During these visions, for they were not quite dreams, Joel used to see a very old man whom he recognized as his grandfather and who told him to go to his home and fetch his hat and other special clothes and equipment which he had used when he was alive

[1] Abdominal pains.

and practised as a *nganga*; the old man also told him to bring his spear and knobkerrie.[1] The young man went to his grandfather's home at Mount Darwin, found these things, and returned to school. But after this his grandfather's *mudzimu* used to enter him during the day as well and sometimes when he was in the classroom, so the principal of the school eventually asked him to leave. When he reached his village he again became seriously ill. He refused the porridge given to him by his parents and lived on raw mealie meal and wild fruit, and ate grass like the cattle. His parents consulted a *nganga*, who told them that the boy's grandfather, who died before he was born, wished to possess their son and make him a *nganga*. Joel's father was instructed to return to his father's home and hold a ceremony at which a bull was to be sacrificed to the spirit. But as he was a poor man, and perhaps not entirely convinced, he refused. That same night after he had returned from the diviner, he was standing near the fire in his hut and the flames 'began to fight him and would not leave him' until his arms and face had been badly burnt. Later, while he was asleep, he dreamt that someone was outside the hut waiting to speak to him. He woke up and went outside, and saw a lion sitting in front of him. He clapped his hands exclaiming: 'This is my father.'[2] The lion did not move, so he went to wake Joel, who was still sick, but when the two of them came out the lion had disappeared.

Joel walked over to the spot where the lion had sat and the *mudzimu* entered him and throughout the night the grandfather's spirit spoke to his son through his grandson. The father was now convinced that his son was possessed by his father's spirit, and arranged for a ceremony; he pre-

---

[1] A stick fashioned from a root of tough wood with a knob at the end. Sometimes used as an offensive weapon.
[2] The Mashona believe that at important times, a tribal or family spirit takes temporary possession of a lion; whenever a lion appears in a village the people become suspicious of the reason for its appearance and go to the *nganga* to find out if a *mudzimu* is displeased.

pared the beer and gave his son a mat but he still did not kill a bull. At the ceremony the spirit entered the young man, but as no sacrifice was forthcoming it became very angry. That same night the young man left home and led by the spirit he came to Hartley, about seventy miles from his home, where he obtained employment in a shirt factory. Two months later, by which time he had saved some money, the spirit again possessed him and asked for its ceremony and sacrifice. By then Joel had married, so his wife prepared the beer and this time a goat was killed at the ceremony. This apparently satisfied the *mudzimu*, for since then Joel has enjoyed excellent health and his practice is a flourishing one. He is a herbalist as well as a diviner and dreams about all kinds of herbs, about the patients who are going to consult him and the treatment they should be given. He has never learnt from another *nganga*, does not use *hakata* but divines only when possessed by his grandfather's healing spirit which he claims has taught him all he knows and in whose honour he holds a ceremony three times a year.

To sum up some of the results of these interrogations:

Seven of the *nganga* fell ill when their healing spirits first indicated that they should become *nganga* and five of these admitted to a state of mental confusion; one *nganga* did not himself become ill but his young relations did and this sickness continued in the family until he accepted the spiritual behest; two of the *nganga* suffered no initial illness.

Six of the *nganga* were apprenticed to other *nganga* and received some form of medical instruction. The remaining four served no apprenticeship and attributed their knowledge entirely to the guidance of their spirit.

All ten *nganga* claimed to be spiritually endowed. Eight inherited their healing spirit from a deceased *nganga* in the family and described the spirit as a *mudzimu*, that is, ancestral spirit, which implies that this healing spirit had been in the family for several generations; two of the *nganga* were endowed with *shave* spirits, one inherited his from a grandmother, but the second was selected by a healing *shave* as it were for the first time, there being no record of a previous *nganga* in the family.

Seven of the *nganga* told me that dreams played an essential part in the successful treatment of their patients. They categorically affirmed that in these dreams their healing spirits showed them all they needed to know—where to find the herbs, their precise uses and how to dispense them; if a patient had a complaint that did not respond to normal treatment, they were confident that the efficacious treatment would come to them during the night.

I was struck by the fact that so high a proportion of these apparently intelligent men and women claimed that dreaming constituted an integral part of their medical knowledge. This claim of learning through dreams is made so constantly by *nganga*, not only in Rhodesia but as far afield as Zululand, that one cannot help feeling it is worthy of further investigation. The phenomenon bears out the important role the subconscious plays in the thought processes of the primitive African, and it suggests that the solution of the *nganga*'s problems in dreams may be due to a capacity to think and reason with his subconscious mind.

Paul Radin[1] draws attention to the importance of the emotional instability and highly defined sensitivity of the medicine man of Siberia and of the Eskimos, not only during the period of initiation, but also after he is established as a *shaman*[2] and is practising his art. Radin says that the initial period of suffering lasts many months and is necessary to authenticate the novice's contact with the spiritual world. The *shaman* goes through the mental phases of suffering, isolation and trance and eventually arrives at a new normality

[1] P. Radin, *Primitive Religion: Its Nature and Origin*, Dover Publications, New York.
[2] Equivalent of *nganga*.

and reintegration. The *shaman* appears to differ from the *nganga* in several aspects. Firstly, as we have seen in the case of two of the *nganga*, suffering is not a *sine qua non* for the novice *nganga*; secondly, where illness was suffered prior to the acceptance of the healing spirit, the *nganga* recovered immediately he accepted his *shave* or *mudzimu*. Suffering, in fact, is only a feature of the *nganga*'s initiation in so far as it is a means of revealing its spiritual cause. Finally, the *nganga*, unlike the *shaman*, is not 'emotionally unstable' nor does he possess, as far as one can judge, the *shaman*'s 'highly defined sensitivity'.

In fact, all ten of the *nganga* I have described were both physically and mentally normal. As personalities they were pleasant and well balanced, with a good control of their emotions and of average or higher-than-average intelligence. I have seen many of them on different occasions since and had no reason to change my opinion.

CHAPTER 2

Analysis of my patients' visits to their nganga

In December 1960 I started asking my Shona patients whether they had consulted diviners to find out the cause of their illnesses. I did not expect all of them to admit they had, as I felt that some would consider these visits as something very private. Each patient was asked after his arrival at the hospital, but not necessarily on the day of his admission, if he had received treatment from a *nganga*. What follows is a summary of what we elicited from twenty-three patients, admitted consecutively and all adult African men.

CASE I. RAYMOND: a Makorekore aged twenty years, admitted with pains in his abdomen and joints. He consulted a *nganga* in November 1959, who said he was bewitched by poison which had been added to his meat. The *nganga* treated him by applying his mouth to various parts of Raymond's body in order to 'suck' out the evil. He felt a little better after this. But as the pains returned, in June 1960, he consulted another *nganga*. This doctor also said that he was being harmed by a witch and told him that she was the wife of his sister's brother-in-law. Raymond could think of no reason for her enmity. The *nganga* made incisions over the patient's chest and back. He improved only slightly after this treatment.

CASE 2. KAUFI: aged forty, was admitted suffering from

paraplegia. He said he was a Roman Catholic and so would not go to a diviner, but he discovered that his wife had gone on his behalf and had been told that his illness was due to a *mudzimu*, that of his grandfather. No action, however, was taken to propitiate the guardian spirit.

CASE 3. GOULAS: aged thirty-two, was from Mrewa. He had been ill with diarrhoea for three days. When he had suffered from the same complaint previously, a diviner had told him that it was because he had not bought a cloth for his grandmother's spirit when she had died in 1955, and that unless he purchased a black one he would not recover. He bought the cloth and offered it to the spirit saying: 'Here is your *fuko*, make me better,' and on that occasion he recovered; this time he did not consult a diviner before coming to the hospital.

CASE 4. NYAMYARO: a MuZezuru[1] aged thirty-eight, came from Marandellas. Three weeks after he became ill, his wife consulted a diviner who told her that his grandmother's spirit wanted beer. Some time before this, when another member of the family was ill, a cow had been sacrificed to the grandmother's spirit, but the final ceremony of beer-offering[2] had been omitted. This had upset the spirit which had shown its annoyance by making Nyamyaro ill.

CASE 5. MUSAVENGI: a MuZezuru aged about forty. His father had died three years before and Musavengi had been ill for a year. When he first complained of a sore throat he had visited a diviner, whose *hakata* showed that his father's spirit wanted a bull to be named after it.[3] The *nganga*'s fee for the divination was five shillings. Musavengi named a bull

---

[1] A member of the Vazezuru tribe who come from the central part of Mashonaland.

[2] A ceremony called *mweredzo*.

[3] *gono romusha*, described in chapter II. Musavengi's father was also a grandfather, so his spirit qualified for this ceremony.

after the spirit of his father and brewed the beer. He felt a little better after this, but his improvement was not maintained.

CASE 6. FRANCIS: a MuZezuru from Enkeldoorn, aged thirty. He suffered from epilepsy and had his first fit in 1950 and since then had had an attack every three years. A year before coming to hospital, he had consulted a diviner who told him that the spirit of his late wife was annoyed with him for refusing to marry her sister; it was so annoyed that it was operating as an angered spirit—a *ngozi*. First it troubled her own parents and they consulted a *nganga* who diverted it back to Francis; it was then that his epilepsy started. In 1959 he married his sister-in-law but he still suffered from fits, so he sought advice from a *nganga* who suggested that he chase the *ngozi* back to the father-in-law, and gave him herbal remedies for the fits. Francis took the medicine, but up to the time he came into the hospital he had not arranged with the *nganga* to drive the *ngozi* to his father-in-law.

CASE 7. GIDEON: a MuZezuru admitted with a pulmonary complaint. The first *nganga* he consulted said that his food had been poisoned by a witch and advised him to see another *nganga* who had the right medicine to induce vomiting and severe purgation, and so drive the poison from his system. Gideon visited this *nganga* and his reaction to the medicine was so violent that not only were his bowels and bladder opened, but he vomited at the same time. After this he felt much better for a week, but during the ensuing one the cough and chest discomfort began to return. He attributed this relapse to the fact that the *nganga* did not have enough of the medicine to give him a full dose. His condition deteriorated so rapidly that he decided to come to hospital. When asked who the witch was, he said it was one of his father's wives and that she had put poison in his porridge.

A *nganga* in full regalia: the hat is of ostrich feathers and the horns suspended from the neck are filled with special medicines

A young *nganga* is accepted as a doctor with a *MaRozvi shave*. She kneels in front of her equipment, holding two medicinal calabashes in her hands

Above left, a woman *nganga*, holding an axe, is seated beside her mother-in-law, also a *nganga*. Her husband (on the right) acts as her acolyte and interpreter when she talks to her patients through her *shave* spirit

Below left, a *nganga* looks into her mirror while her acolyte calls on her *shave* to enter her; the patient sits facing them

Above, three women *nganga* who practise through a *shave* spirit

A *nganga* practising in a rural district of Mashonaland; his
stick is carved in a snake design

CASE 8. SINOWA: aged fifty-five, complained of general weakness of the body and indeed was unable to walk on admission to hospital. His illness had started a month earlier and he had sent his wife to a diviner to find out the reason. The *nganga* found that it was due to the spirit of his grandmother, which wanted a she-goat to be sacrificed to it and beer to be brewed. The spirit was annoyed because it wanted to be remembered and the customary service in its honour had been omitted for a long time. The *nganga* said that Sinowa should first undergo treatment in a European hospital and that he could make the sacrifice to the grandmother's spirit when he recovered.

CASE 9. DUNYWA: was admitted with pain of three months' duration over the upper abdomen. Clinical diagnosis was of a primary carcinoma of the liver. The patient had consulted a diviner, who had declared that his illness was due to his grandmother's spirit, which wanted a beer ceremony and a cloth. At the same time, the *nganga* had treated him with certain herbs. But although Dunywa had brewed the beer and bought the cloth his health did not improve.

CASE 10. JOSEPH: a Makorekore aged about thirty-eight. In August 1959 he had consulted a diviner because of pain in his chest. The *nganga* said that he was sick because he had failed to hold the ceremony of *kurova guva*[1] for his father. Joseph did not believe this diagnosis and saw another *nganga*, who said he had not paid back all the dowry money he had borrowed from his father when he married, and, in fact, Joseph owed his father £7 which he had not repaid before his death. This *nganga* also told him that his aunt (the wife of his late father's brother) knew about this debt and

[1] Literal translation is 'to beat the grave'. An important ritual which takes place about a year after death is the last visit to the grave. Beer is prepared and all relatives and friends attend the ceremony. The precincts of the grave are swept, beer is poured over the grave and the spirit is believed to be finally put to rest.

that she had gone to his father's grave and said to his spirit: 'Go to your son and ask for the money, now that you are dead.' The patient was so impressed with this *nganga*'s divination that he paid the money, and the pain in his chest lessened, but after a time he developed diarrhoea. This time he did not consult another *nganga*.

CASE II. MBAVIMBVI: a MuZezuru aged forty, admitted with unresolved pneumonia. He had been suffering with chest pains and a cough for a month prior to admission to hospital. His nephew had consulted a diviner who said that Mbavimbvi had not returned a cow to his mother before her death. Her spirit was now a *ngozi* and had caused the illness. By this time the patient was in hospital, but the nephew replaced the cow and eventually Mbavimbvi recovered and left hospital.

CASE 12. MATOKE: an adult MuBudya[2] suffering from primary carcinoma of the liver. In 1960 he had complained of abdominal pains and dark urine and had consulted a *nganga*. The *nganga* told him that his grandfather's spirit wanted beer because it had not been honoured with a ceremony for a long time. Matoke brewed the beer, but his health did not improve, so he returned to the same *nganga*, who then advised him to seek a different diviner. The next *nganga* told him that a hunting *shave* wanted to be accepted by him and that until he agreed to accept it and carry out its wishes he would not recover. Matoke's father refused to believe this diagnosis and advised him to see a European doctor in the district.

CASE 13. MHERE: aged seventy-three, came from the Chikwakwa reserve. He had been a member of the Apostolic Church for the past ten years and was therefore forbidden

[2] A Shona sub-tribe living close to the Portuguese border on the Eastern part of Mashonaland.

to consult a diviner. Two months before admission to hospital, he began to discharge pus from his scrotum and penis; he left the church and sent his son to a diviner on his behalf. The son was told that his father's illness was due to a *ngozi*—his wife's spirit which was angered because when her husband had moved to a new village he took with him the two cows given to her when her two daughters had married. They were subsequently slaughtered and never replaced, and it was because of this that his wife's spirit had made him ill. Mhere did not replace the cows.

CASE 14. LANGTON: a Makorekore, complained of painful legs and right-sided chest pain. He had once consulted a *nganga* but not in connection with his illness; he was a hunter, and when he found that his dogs were no longer finding game, he consulted a *nganga* who told him that he was unsuccessful because a *bveni*[1] *shave* wished to possess him. He told Langton to make a *tsambo*[2] of blue beads for it. The patient told us that after he had done this he was able to find plenty of game again.

CASE 15. GAWEMBI: from the Seke reserve, was admitted with an amoebic liver abscess. During 1960 he began to complain of pain on the right side of the abdomen, and his father consulted a *nganga* on his behalf. The diviner threw his *hakata* and found that the illness was due to the spirit of the patient's grandmother which was annoyed because no ceremony had been held for her since her death. Gawembi refused to believe this and told his father that he was coming into hospital.

CASE 16. NZAREA: sixty-five years old, from Mrewa, admitted to hospital suffering from pulmonary tuberculosis. When he first became ill, the year before, his two sisters had sought advice from a diviner who said he was ill because the

[1] Baboon spirit.
[2] Necklace.

spirit of their grandfather wanted a bull to be killed and that this ceremony must be followed by another—a beer-offering also in his honour. These directions were carried out but the patient said that his health did not improve.

CASE 17. NERA: aged forty, a MuZezuru from Seke. In April 1960 he began to complain of an intractable cough, so he consulted a diviner who found that a witch was responsible. He did not believe this *nganga* because he would not name the witch, so he consulted another *nganga* who said that he was ill because his grandfather's spirit wanted a bull to be named after it. Nera did this but the animal died shortly afterwards, which for some reason made him doubt the accuracy of the *nganga*'s diagnosis. A third *nganga* told him that his grandmother's spirit was to blame and that it wanted her two cows to be returned to her own family. Nera was convinced that this was the real reason for his illness and sent the two cows back to his grandmother's family, but still the cough continued.

CASE 18. CHEGA: aged fifty, admitted with a gastric complaint of a year's duration. When the illness began he consulted a *nganga* who declared that a witch had poisoned him. Chega did not accept this diagnosis and sought a second opinion. The second *nganga* confirmed the findings of the first one. Chega then consulted a third *nganga* who also corroborated what the other two had said. Not one of them, however, would name the witch, and though he took the medicines that were prescribed by the last *nganga*, his health did not improve and he continued to suffer abdominal pains.

CASE 19. SIMON: admitted to the hospital with a liver disorder, suspected cirrhosis. In March 1961, when the right side of his abdomen had been swollen for about six months, he sent his brother to consult a *nganga*. His *hakata* revealed that Simon's illness was caused by a witch; for this piece of divination the brother was charged one shilling. Simon was unwilling to accept the diviner's diagnosis because he had not named the witch, but to be absolutely certain, he asked his mother to consult a second *nganga*, who confirmed that he was bewitched, but in spite of this unanimity, Simon decided to be treated in a Government hospital.

CASE 20. JAFIES: a Makorekore aged twenty-four, admitted with asthma of one year's duration. At the beginning of 1961, when he was first troubled with tight breathing, he sent his sister to a *nganga*. She was told that the asthma was caused by his mother's spirit—it wanted a beer ceremony to be held in its honour. This opinion cost one shilling. Beer was prepared and the ceremony took place, but Jafies' breathing failed to improve.

CASE 21. ANTONIO: a forty-year-old MuZezuru, admitted with a diagnosis of cancer of the stomach. He had begun to experience abdominal pain five months previously and after two months consulted a diviner, who attributed the illness to the spirit of his grandmother, which wanted a cow and had sent a witch to poison him. He was given medicines and charged £2. 5s. od. for them. But as they made him no better he sought a second *nganga*, who attributed the illness directly to a witch. The name of the witch was not given, but the *nganga* gave him some medicines which cost £1. 5. 0. These also did nothing to improve his condition so he consulted a third *nganga*. In spite of the £3 he paid for medicines as a result of this third consultation, he was still no better.

CASE 22. MURELSI: a MuZezuru, aged forty, admitted with cirrhosis of the liver. Since September 1960 he had been considerably troubled with a cough, abdominal pain and diarrhoea. He had been treated by herbalists for some time but without relief. In April, 1961, he consulted a diviner

who said that his illness was due to the activity of a witch—
he said it was a woman who lived in his village. The
nganga prescribed herbs to remove the witch's poison, but
as they did not help Murelsi went to a Government clinic.

CASE 23. SUMINE: a MuZezuru aged thirty, from the
Urungwe reserve. He had been ill for nearly a year with
abdominal pains and, on admission to hospital, was found
to be suffering from carcinoma of the liver. In December
1960 his father had consulted a *nganga* who told him that the
spirit of the patient's grandmother had caused the illness
because it wanted beer to be brewed and a ceremony held in
its honour. The spirit's wishes were carried out but the
patient was no better. His father saw another diviner who
claimed that the illness was due to the spirit of Sumine's
grandfather and that it wanted a beer ceremony. Again the
ritual was carried out and the spirit honoured in the usual
way. But this too proved of no avail, and the patient felt there
was no alternative but to try the medicine of the European
doctors.

A study of these case histories shows that between the onset
of illness and admission to my wards these twenty-three
patients had consulted thirty-four diviners. All but one
(who had refused treatment) had been unsuccessfully treated
by *nganga* for the relief of their symptoms; it is fair to add
that most of their illnesses were of a chronic and serious
nature.

On fifteen occasions, the spirit guardians were held
responsible for the illnesses. The spirits of the grandmother
and grandfather were each mentioned seven times. I should
hesitate to conclude from this that the grandmother's spirit
is found to be the cause of illness as frequently as that of the
grandfather. This is not a large enough series of cases to
disprove what the Mashona maintain—that the spirit of the

grandfather being the most important in the family, is the one most often responsible for sickness. Next in frequency came the witch, who was blamed in twelve consultations. An aggrieved spirit was diagnosed five times, and an alien spirit twice.

I was interested to find that these figures corroborated what I have recorded elsewhere in my field studies, namely that the spirits diagnosed by the *nganga* in their order of importance as causes of illness were—to give them their Shona names—the *mudzimu*, the *muroyi*, the *ngozi*, and the *shave*.

CHAPTER 3

Witchcraft cases
heard in the law courts of Mashonaland

Since the Southern Rhodesian Witchcraft Suppression Ordinance was issued in 1899 any person who is accused of being a witch can bring his accusers to Court. The back history of these Court cases follows roughly the same pattern —a Shona, suspecting that he is a victim of witchcraft, consults a *nganga* who corroborates his fears and names, in spite of the penalties, the person who has bewitched his client. The so-called witch, upset by the accusation and the resulting ostracism and probable victimization, goes to the police and reports the *nganga* who has 'named' him. He brings this action partly in a spirit of revenge and partly in order to have his name cleared.

The reason I include some of these cases here is that they show more clearly than any generalizations on Shona beliefs could how the African is unable to accept any out of the ordinary event, however trivial, as accidental or simply as 'bad luck'. If illness or death follows an event of this kind, there must, he argues, be a reason and if the *nganga* can find no spiritual cause then the unexplained event and subsequent illness must be the work of a witch. Envy, a quarrel, the display of anger, an incident—which we should call an accident —all set in motion the cult of the witch hunt. In nearly every case I looked at in the Police records the person accused of practising witchcraft was either a relation, or someone in close contact with the so-called victim, and therefore in a position to 'doctor' the food or place a spell in his hut. In the majority of cases the witch was a woman.

In the ten cases I have selected, the *nganga* plays his traditional role of 'smelling out the witch'. But in practice it very often happens that the Shona who suspects someone of practising witchcraft against him is so overwrought and unable to control himself that he accuses an individual himself without waiting to consult a *nganga*, often physically attacking and injuring the suspected witch.

CASE 1 brought by Mwaringiseni: an adult Shona woman living in an African village in the south of Mashonaland. Her mother, Makufa, also had two sons, one of whom was called Levi and who died of a snake bite in April, 1961. A few days after he died, his brother told Mwaringiseni that she must accompany their mother, Makufa, together with other relatives, to a *nganga* in order to learn why Levi had been bitten by the snake. When the party arrived at his village, the *nganga*, a man called Muchurhura, announced that he knew why they had come to see him: 'You have come to me to throw the bones. Someone has died at your village of a snake bite.' Mwaringiseni was impressed because no one had told the *nganga* the reason for their visit. The family took up their position, sitting in a semi-circle round Muchurhura. Before throwing the *hakata* he asked for 26/-, which was handed to him by Levi's father. After the first throw Muchurhura declared that the person responsible was present with them, and asked each of the relatives in turn to throw the bones, starting with the father whom he pronounced innocent. The last to throw was Mwaringiseni. The *nganga* asked her to throw again and said excitedly: 'You are right. You are the one who sent the snake to bite the person.' Mwaringiseni argued and protested her innocence but Muchurhura continued to accuse her. The party returned to their village and a few nights later Mwaringiseni was awakened by the sound of fire. Her hut was alight and she tried to run out of it but as she got to the doorway she received two blows on the head. She turned and saw that it was her brother who had hit her. Mwaringiseni reported the *nganga*, Muchurhura, to the police and he was found guilty by the court.

CASE 2 brought by Smart, a Shona in the employment of a European estate at Melsetter. At the beginning of September, 1961, he was involved in an accident; he was driving a lorry down a steep bank on one of the farm roads and was forced to swerve suddenly in order to avoid a stone. Immediately after the accident, he jumped out of the lorry to look for the stone but could not find it. This made Smart suspicious and he went to a *nganga* called Chigive to ask his advice. Chigive produced a small box from which he removed his *hakata* and a mirror. After throwing the *hakata* he told Smart that a responsible person employed on the same estate, probably the 'boss boy', had caused the accident; Smart named the two 'boss boys' and Chigive declared that the one named Machone was the one who was to blame. Smart could not understand this as he had never had an argument with Machone so he reported Chigive to the police and the court found him guilty.[1]

CASE 3 brought by Mariot, one of seven brothers, and employed by a large firm in Salisbury. He lived in an African township just outside the town. His father had owned a small farm some thirty miles outside Salisbury and when he died in March 1956, he left the farm to Mariot's elder brother, Mackenzie. This inheritance caused constant friction between the brothers and none of them were on good terms with Mackenzie. In May 1961, Mariot learned that Mackenzie had developed foot trouble and that he,

---

[1] The reason why Smart reported the *nganga* is probably because he felt cheated at having paid for the consultation, and because the *nganga* had 'named' a person with whom he was friendly.

Mariot, was believed to have bewitched him. The foot complaint had started one day when Mackenzie was walking barefooted over his land and injured his right big toe. Three days later he sent for a *nganga* called Musenda who declared that Mariot was responsible. As soon as he heard what had happened, Mariot went to Mackenzie and insisted that he accompany him to see Musenda. But when they arrived at his home, the *nganga* denied having accused Mariot although he admitted that he had said that Mackenzie had been bewitched. Unable to control his temper, Mariot took hold of the *nganga* by the wrist and beat him with a whip. Not satisfied with this physical revenge, Mariot reported the *nganga* to the police and Musenda was decreed guilty by the court.

CASE 4 brought by Rosie, a married woman living with her husband, Sungayi, in a village in an African reserve. Also living in the same village was a man called Amos, whose brother had died recently. Amos went to a *nganga* called Mapize to find out the cause of his brother's death and took his friend Sungayi with him. Mapize declared that the death was caused by Rosie, the wife of Sungayi. He came to this conclusion after the names of the people in the village were said out loud to him by the two men while he threw the bones to find out which was guilty. When they got to the name of Sungayi, he announced in a loud voice for all to hear: 'It is the wife of Sungayi who has caused the death.' The two men returned to the village and all the men of the village were called to a meeting at the *dare* where the headman stood up and told them that Sungayi's wife was responsible for the death. Rosie went to the police and Mapize, the *nganga*, was judged guilty.

CASE 5 brought by Mafanato who lived with her husband, Muchemwe, on a large ranch. In the rainy season of 1959, Mafanato had held a beer party in her hut. The next day

Mafanato gave her husband and his second wife, Joano, the beer left over from the previous night. While they were drinking it, Paul, a friend of Muchemwe, came into the hut and was invited to have some beer which they all drank out of the same tin. The following morning Paul fell ill and died that afternoon. Neither Joano, Mafanato nor Muchemwe suffered any ill effects from the beer. A few days later, Paul's brother, Jackias, and his widow, Rosy, went with Muchemwe, Joano and Mafanato to a *nganga* who declared that Paul had been bewitched. Without waiting for him to name the witch, Rosy accused Mafanato, as it was she who had brewed the beer. Rosy struck her three times on her head and Jackias kicked Muchemwe, Mafanato's husband, in the chest. Mafanato complained to the authorities and the court found Rosy guilty.

CASE 6 brought by Masodzi, the second wife of a man called Ringisayi. By his first wife he had a son, Kumirayi, who by this time was married with a son of his own. On 17th July, 1959, Kumirayi entered the hut of Masodzi, who was sitting with her young son Takwana; he took hold of the boy and attacked him with his open hands so fiercely that Takwana fell to the ground. In his temper, Kumirayi shouted at Masodzi: 'I assault your son because you are the one who bewitched my son and my wife. Yes, you are the one because I was told so by the *nganga*.' Masodzi first reported Kumirayi to the chief who refused to intervene and referred the complainant to the Police. In court, Kumirayi gave no reason why he suspected Masodzi of being a witch. He was found guilty.

CASE 7 brought by Sibuye, a Shona woman living in the same village as her father-in-law, Nyika, who was headman of the village. On 2nd February, 1960, when Sibuye's husband was lying ill in his hut, Nyika came to the entrance and stood in the doorway, but did not enter the hut. A short time later, Nyika, who had meanwhile seen a *nganga* about his son's illness, returned to the hut with his brother and without any further ado they carried off Sibuye's husband. The distraught woman followed them, whereupon Nyika accused her of being a witch and of having bewitched his son. Sibuye went to the police and reported her father-in-law who was found guilty.

CASE 8 brought by Kahwahwa, married for twenty years to a man called Sindi. One day, a year after two of their children had died, Kahwahwa was sitting in her husband's hut when he came close to her and said: 'You know, my wife, you are the one who killed all my children and ate them. You are a witch.' Two days later Sindi again accused his wife and demanded that her father return the *lobolo* and that Kahwahwa undergo a trial by ordeal. He took her to another village to Kasimbo, a man who specialized in these trials, and who gave her the special medicine to drink. She failed to vomit and Kasimbo announced for all to hear[1] that Kahwahwa was a witch. She was taken back by her own family to the village of one of her brothers but he sent her back to Sindi, accusing Sindi of being himself a witch, declaring that he had sucked the breasts of Kahwahwa.[2] Sindi denied this but agreed to undergo a similar ordeal and, like Kahwahwa, failed to vomit before witnesses. This proved to Kahwahwa and her family that Sindi was the witch. The court found both Sindi and Kahwahwa guilty as each had accused the other.

CASE 9 brought by Nyobazi, a woman living in an African village, in a hut close to that of the headman's wife, Chizuva. In July 1958, Chizuva lost her baby and a few weeks later

[1] The presence of witnesses is an important factor in the naming of witches.
[2] A significant accusation, because any unnatural action suggests a witch.

she accused Nyobazi of being a witch and of having killed her child, and she ordered Nyobazi not to build her new hut near to hers in the new part of the village. These accusations were made at a beer party held in Nyobazi's hut and for that reason Nyobazi decided to take no notice of them. But in July the following year another of Chizuva's children died and Chizuva decided to consult a *nganga* about the two deaths. The *nganga* confirmed her suspicions and pronounced Nyobazi a witch. Armed with this information, Chizuva went straight to Nyobazi's hut and again accused her and ordered her to go and live in another part of the village. In the evidence during the subsequent court case there was an inference that Nyobazi had suckled the first baby[1] who had died.

CASE 10 concerns two brothers, both of whom were married. Urayayi, married to Aginess, lived on a European farm where he was employed, and Tobias and his wife worked on a neighbouring farm. In July 1959 Urayayi heard that a child of his brother Tobias had died, so according to Shona custom he and Aginess went to Tobias's place of employment to pay their respects. After the burial, when all were gathered in his hut, Tobias shouted: 'My brother, you are married to a witch. If you don't divorce your wife, I will never come to your home. I have some money and if you get another wife I will give it to you to pay your *lobolo*. You won't leave here till we go together to see a *nganga*. Your wife was responsible for the death of my other child in 1957 and you refused then to come to the *nganga*.' Tobias went on to say that his wife had had a quarrel with Aginess in 1959 over some goats which had strayed and four days later his infant child had died. Tobias now lost all control and knocked Aginess down and kicked her in the chest. Urayayi agreed to accompany Tobias to the *nganga*, but when they got there the diviner, after throwing the *hakata*, found Tobias

[1] A witch is believd to pass evil into a baby that she suckles.

to be the witch and announced him responsible for the death of his own child. Aginess meanwhile had reported Tobias to the police and he was found guilty.

It is difficult to assess how much the findings of a European Court affect the main participants once the case is over. I do not think, for instance, that the reputation of a *nganga* would necessarily suffer as a result of being found guilty by the Court. The majority of his clients would maintain— as I have heard them do so often—that it is impossible for Europeans to understand Shona beliefs as they do not belong to the same spiritual world.

The fines imposed for naming a witch are fairly severe and prison sentences vary from two months to two years.

PART III

Herbal Remedies Used by
Two Particular Nganga

CHAPTER I

The general preparation of herbs

Some time ago I studied the methods of two herbalist *nganga* in considerable detail. One of these men practised in Mrewa, fifty miles outside Salisbury, the other at Sipolilo which is about a hundred and fifty miles from the city.[1] I include some of the notes I took at this time in the hope that they may interest herbalists outside Africa. I have tried, wherever possible, to give the Latin as well as the Shona name of the various plants and trees.

But before examining the remedies for specific illnesses used by these two men, it is worth taking a quick look at the different ways herbs are prepared as these are used by all herbalist *nganga*. Herbalists collect all the ingredients for their medicines themselves, they find them mostly in the bush where they dig for roots, search for special plants and collect leaves, bark off trees, and anything else they may require. A herbalist cleans what he has gathered before setting about the actual preparation of the medicine which, of course, varies according to the form in which it is going to be prescribed to the patient.

TO CRUSH A ROOT INTO FINE POWDER: After the root has dried in the sun for three days, the hard outside layer is removed and the inside is crushed between two stones.[2] The

---

[1] He has since moved to Salisbury where he has a herbal practice in the African township of Harare.

[2] This process is known as *kukuya* and in some remedies the outside layer is also retained and ground to powder.

bigger stone is placed on the ground and the smaller one is held in the palm of the other hand, the root being ground between them until it is reduced to a fine powder. If the root is large, it is first broken into smaller pieces and beaten in a stamping block. The powder is stored in a horn, or nowadays in an ordinary medicine bottle, and it is prescribed in two ways. If the patient is a child, a tablespoonful of the powder is put into a small pot containing half a glass of water, a little meal is added and the mixture stirred with a small stick while it cooks. This thin porridge, called *bota*, is poured on to a wooden plate and drunk by the patient when it is cool. For an adult the powder is added to his ordinary stiff porridge (*sadza*). The herbalist explains exactly how the powder should be cooked with the *bota* or the *sadza* and leaves a supply of powder with the family so that it can be given to the patient twice a day.

Sometimes the powder is made of more than one root, and may include leaves and the bark of trees as well.

TO PREPARE SPECIAL POWDER USED IN SKIN IN-CISIONS: The roots are cleaned with a knife to remove sand or mud and are put into a *chaenga*[1]. After the roots have burnt down to ashes, the *chaenga* is removed from the fire and a little castor oil[2] is added to moisten the ashes. The mixture[3] is stored in a small calabash, horn or a bottle. This medicine is prescribed for painful ailments, particularly for pains in the chest and back. The herbalist makes a short incision with his knife over the painful area (usually about a centimetre long), moistens the tip of his little finger by spitting on it and dips it into the ash which he rubs into the cut.[4] There are variations of this medicine, sometimes the roots

---

[1] Broken clay pot; when a pot breaks the larger piece is always kept and is used for roasting food, like peanuts etc., or by the *nganga* for burning roots.

[2] From the seed of the *futa* tree, in Shona it is called *mafuta* oil.

[3] Known as *mushonga wakapiswa*.

[4] These incisions are known as *nyora*.

are only partially burnt, giving a charcoal powder called *tsito*; a herbalist may mix this with an ash-reduced root, or with powder from an unburnt root. If there is no alleviation of pain after the first treatment, the herbalist makes another incision and repeats the treatment.

POWDER USED FOR NASAL INSTILLATIONS: The roots are broken into small pieces, pounded on a stamping block into smaller, fragments and dried in the sun. After being ground the very fine powder is stored in a horn or the handle of a calabash. The patient sniffs this medicine which has the same effect as snuff and makes him sneeze. Herbalists also make ordinary medical snuff which they prescribe for headaches.

POWDER USED FOR INSUFFLATIONS: This powder is also very finely ground, and the only difference in the preparation is that after the root is pounded into small pieces it is thoroughly dried over a fire instead of in the sun. The herbalist blows this powder through a hollow reed into the patient's rectum. He prescribes this treatment in illnesses characterized by long-continued fever; if the patient fails to improve with powder made from roots or dried herbs, he may change to green leaves which are crushed into tiny pieces and blown through the reed in the same way as the powder.

TO PREPARE LIQUID MEDICINE: The roots or herbs are either crushed into small pieces between two stones, the process being halted before they become pulverized, or they are ground down in a stamping block. The bits are then soaked in a pot of water for anything from one to fourteen days, depending on the type of root. The water in which the herbs or roots have been steeped is drunk either neat or added to the patient's porridge. After about a week, the water is changed and freshly crushed roots are added to the new water.

Medicine prepared by this steeping method is used to treat chronic coughs; if flesh or fowl is added for nutritional purposes the mixture is boiled after the stamping process.

USE OF LEAVES: Fresh green leaves are pounded in a stamping block and then pressed into a round ball called a *chigodo* which is left to dry in the sun for three days. On the fourth day the *chigodo* is put into water and soaked overnight and the next morning the water is ready to be used, usually mixed in a thin porridge.

Dried leaves are used for medicinal smoking. After drying in the sun for a day, the leaves are crushed into small pieces, packed in a reed and smoked like a cigarette.[1]

Leaves are also used as a means of applying heat to the body. They are boiled in a pot and placed on the affected part of the body while still hot. When they cool they are reboiled and used again. Each leaf is left on the patient for ten to twenty minutes; the treatment is supposed to last for half an hour every morning and evening for three weeks and the same leaves are used throughout the treatment.[2]

INHALATIONS: These are prepared from various herbal ingredients, but one in common use is made from the leaves and roots of the *murovamhodzi* tree. The roots are cut into small pieces and placed in a pot of water with the leaves and cooked. This is done just before the treatment. After the mixture has boiled for about an hour, the *nganga* removes his patient's shirt, sits him on the ground, covers his head with a blanket, places the boiling pot under the blanket and instructs him to inhale the fumes until there is no more steam.

Another inhalation is made from roots alone, and they

[1] Roots are also used in this way, particularly the root of the *mumbanda* tree (Tagetes minuta).

[2] Leaves from *dovakamwe* and *zumbani* (Lippia jevanica) are commonly used in this treatment.

are cut into small pieces and cooked without water in a *chaenga*. When the roots begin to smoke the *chaenga* is removed from the fire and the patient, his head and shoulders covered by a blanket, is told to inhale.

HERBAL PREPARATIONS TAKEN WITH FOOD: The herbs (crushed roots are also used) are cooked overnight in a soup of beans and drunk by the patient in the morning. This treatment is prescribed for three days, a fresh pot of soup and herbs being cooked each night.[1]

OINTMENTS: Are made from a variety of ingredients, usually the basis is sap from a tree which is collected in a small vessel placed underneath incisions cut in the trunk. Various roots are prepared and added to the sap, the mixture boiled in a little water and poured into a calabash. After it has stood for a day the greasy salve is rubbed into the skin which becomes soft as a result. As we have seen, ointments are seldom used for skin complaints, but they are prescribed occasionally as 'skin food' for patients who are losing weight. The fat of the hippopotamus is sometimes added to the tree sap and roots. But ointments, on the whole, are not a very common part of the herbalist's stock in trade.

[1] Often prescribed by the *nganga* in cases of urinary bilharziasis, when the root used is *ndaundau*.

CHAPTER 2

Remedies prescribed by the nganga
from Mrewa

THE TREATMENT OF MHEPO: a typhoid-like illness characterized by a long-continued fever. The *nganga* treats the patient with two different remedies. The first consists of a powder which he prepares from the root of the *mushonjwa* tree, he mixes the powder with *rukweza*[1] meal, fills a reed with the medicine and insufflates it into the patient's rectum. If the patient excretes the powder, he repeats the procedure until the medicine is retained. For the second medicine he mixes the roots of the *muzeze*[2] and *muchenga*[3] and the patient is given the medicine in a liquid porridge.

ROPA MUDODI: blood in the stools. The *nganga* digs up the root of the *Kariringwe* tree, ties some leaves off the tree to the root and places it in the evening in a pot of water with three freshly cut pieces of meat. This is left to soak throughout the night and the patient is instructed to take some of the meat and the liquid the next morning and evening.

CHIBAYO: pneumonia. The *nganga* has three different treatments, he tries each for two or three days and if there is no improvement goes on to the next. For the initial treatment, the *nganga* goes into the bush, faces east and beats the leaves off the nearest tree, he then faces west and repeats the procedure. Only the leaves that fall face upwards are collected,

[1] Eleusine indica.
[2] Albizia adianthifoliar.   [3] Conophanyngia sp.

they are crushed into small pieces and a few drops of water are added. The *nganga* applies the crushed leaves to the painful areas of the chest and holds them there while the patient breathes as deeply as he can. If the patient improves with this treatment the *nganga* continues it until the pneumonia clears.

But if there is still no improvement by the third day, he digs up another kind of root. This time he clears away the soil and cuts a small piece from the exposed root. He picks it up with the point of his knife, taking care not to touch it with his hands, and puts it next to the patient while he goes back and cuts another piece. He moves the two pieces on to the painful area with his big toe[1], and telling the patient to breathe deeply, he steps on the roots with his toe. In the next stage of this treatment, the pieces of root are crushed, dried and ground to a fine powder. The *nganga* makes two incisions over the site of the pain and two on the opposite side of the chest where there is no pain. He spits on his finger, dips it in the powder, and rubs it into the incisions over the painful side only.

If both these treatments fail, the *nganga* still has one more up his sleeve. On the roof of the main hut there are two poles, one runs eastward, the other westward and they join at the top. The *nganga* eats some special medicine, goes up to the roof and takes a small piece of bark off each pole. He burns these pieces in a *chaenga*, mixes the powdered bark with a piece of charcoal which collects on the roof of every hut just above the fireplace, and adds a little salt. He rubs this mixture into incisions over the painful area.

KUKOSORA: persistent cough in small children. Roots of the *gwendere*[2] are crushed and steeped in water in a small calabash; the water is added to the child's thin porridge and

---

[1] There appears to be no reason for the *nganga* not touching the root with his hands, it is merely a ritual in this particular treatment.
[2] Asclepias.

eaten in the morning and evening.[1] The two following days his porridge is mixed with water in which the roots of the *chipariwangona*[2] have soaked. If the sputum clears and the cough is less frequent, the *nganga* stops treatment, but if there is no marked improvement, he burns the roots of the *Gwendere* to ashes and drops the ashes into the child's mouth so that they are inhaled by the bronchi.

KUKOSORA in the adult is treated slightly differently. One of the medicines used is called *mukuru nyarapfuva* and is taken only in the evening, the *nganga* warms the roots over the fire and the patient chews them, swallowing the juice and spitting out the pulp. The treatment is repeated every evening until the cough disappears, but if there is no improvement, the *nganga* digs up *mhingami* roots which he prepares in the same way. If this also fails to relieve the cough, he takes a piece of bark from the east side of a *mubvamaropa*[3] tree and a piece from the west side, then he goes to the nearest pool of water and pulls out a *mahapa*[4] plant (water lily). He throws away the outer layer of the *mahapa* root and crushes the inner part with the bark off the *mubvamaropa* tree, soaks them in water which is later mixed with thin porridge and drunk three times a day by the patient. If the cough still proves obstinate, the *nganga* prescribes a form of cigarette made from the dried leaves of the *muringari*, *mutsubvu* and the *ndebvu* which grows in the *musasa*[5] tree. He crushes the leaves in his hand and puts them in a reed which is lit and smoked like a cigarette, the patient coughing a good deal during the process.

---

[1] To feed a baby with a liquid porridge, the mother lays the child flat, opens its mouth by holding the jaw with one hand, fills the palm of her other hand with porridge and pours it into the mouth. This method of feeding is called *chisuka*; another method known as *kumukika neminwe* is used with children between two or three years of age, the mother dips her index finger in the porridge and puts it in the baby's mouth.

[2] Borreria dibrachiata.   [3] Pterocarpus angolensis.
[4] Nymphaea caerulea.   [5] Brachystegia spiciformis.

Remedies prescribed by the nganga from Mrewa

CHIRWERE OR CHORURINDI: asthma. The *nganga* uses a mistletoe, *gomorara*[1] which grows on the *mukuta*[2] tree, the *mutohwe* tree and on the *mubvamaropa* tree. After collecting mistletoe off these three trees, he fills with water a special pot with a neck, adds the mistletoe and covers it with a lid. He then kills a fowl and puts a leg or a wing into the pot. Next he digs some sandy-like soil from an anthill, and mixes it with water, he puts the pot beside the fire and plasters the join between the neck and the lid with the wet sand, keeping some in reserve to cover any cracks that may appear in the pot and allow the fumes to escape. This heating operation, during which the pot is turned from time to time, lasts all night; at about 6 a.m. the *nganga* removes the pot and puts both hands round it to gauge the temperature. When it is cool and no smoke escapes, he removes the soil from the neck, takes off the lid and gives his patient the flesh of the fowl and some of the broth. The remainder of the bird is cooked in the rest of the liquid during the following three nights and is eaten in the morning.

If the patient still coughs and produces abundant and frothy sputum the *nganga* judges that the time has come to induce vomiting. The medicine is prepared from the roots of the *murutsa*[3] bush, the outer layers are crushed and left to soak overnight in water outside the village. The following morning he takes some *mumera* meal, a wooden plate and a large pot to the spot where he left the *murutsa* roots. At sunset he takes the patient there and makes a thin porridge of the meal and the steeped water and pours it on to the wooden plate to cool. As he gives it to the patient he claps his hands and calls out the name of one of his patient's *mudzimus*, either that of his grandfather or grandmother and asks the spirit to allow the disease to leave the patient.

The patient's relatives, who witness this treatment, clap their hands and say 'We are giving your patient medicine'.

[1] Loranthus spp.   [2] Piliostigma thonningiu.
[3] Bolusanthus speciosus

These words are said this time to please and encourage the *nganga*'s *mudzimu*; this special appeal is made because the treatment is recognized as a drastic one with possibly dangerous consequences. After the patient has drunk the medicine and as soon as he looks as if he were about to vomit, the *nganga* leads him to a spot near a tree and digs a hole into which he vomits or passes excreta. The *nganga* is supposed to be able to tell from the vomit whether the disease has been driven out; he is pleased if the patient rejects not only the medicine but also his food; blood, too, is considered a good sign.

MANYOKA: diarrhoea. The *nganga* treats this complaint very seriously because each year gastro-enteritis carries off hundreds of African children. For this reason he tries to prevent an outbreak by giving all the inhabitants of a village preventive medicine in early September, before the water in the rivers heats up. He digs up a quantity of large roots which look like sweet potatoes and are known to all *nganga* as *muti wezuva*, he cuts each root into six portions and soaks them in water for twenty-four hours. He gathers all the villagers together and gives each a portion and some of the water. The dose is repeated every day for six days, fresh water being added to the roots in the evening.

For those who do not like, or cannot take this medicine, the *nganga* prepares another from the roots of *muchenya*,[1] *katsai* and *chipindura*[2]. The outer layers are crushed together, soaked in water and the liquid added to porridge.

MUSANA: backache. The Mrewa *nganga* classifies backache into three different types according to its cause, which he finds out by throwing the bones for he is a diviner as well as a herbalist.

1. *Musana matyorwa* is caused by a daughter and son-in-law failing to present the wife's parents with a gift at the ritual

[1] Trichilia emetica.   [2] Bolvsanthus speciosus.

ceremony called *masungiro* which should take place soon after their marriage. As a result of this omission, the parents develop severe backache which the *nganga* treats with a medicine made from *chityora badza*, which the mother soaks in water for two days (her daughter is not allowed to see this medicine). She gathers some *muriwo wenyemba*[1] and prepares relish by cooking it with the dried leaves of beans or toasted pumpkin seeds. On the morning of the third day she prepares stiff porridge and puts it in a winnowing basket with the relish. Both parents eat the porridge every morning for three days, always leaving a small portion on their plates which they throw behind them without looking where it falls. After the third day they wash themselves in the water containing the *chityora badza*.

2. *Musana chitsinga*: backache caused by someone buying 'bad' medicine called *chitsinga* and planting this poison in the path of a victim. To treat it, the *nganga* cuts incisions on the patient's back and rubs into the cuts either the powdered roots of the *mhingani*, or another more complicated medicine for which he needs a *gakandye*—a freshwater crab found in pools formed by heavy rains. He removes one of its forelegs and the right hind leg, without killing the unfortunate animal, burns them with the roots of the *chibaya*[2] and the *makono* and dampens the resulting powdered ash with castor oil before rubbing it into the incisions on the patient's back.

3. *Kurwara kwemusana kwokuroyiwa*: backache caused by a witch. The patient either walks or is carried to a crossroads. The *nganga* cuts incisions over the painful area, places his stamping block to mark the exact intersection of the paths and lays his patient face down beside it. He applies his cupping horn to the incisions and collects the blood that oozes from the cuts into a *chaenga*, repeating the cupping until the blood looks a good colour. Patient and stamping block are then removed from the crossroads and the *nganga*

[1] A leafy green vegetable.   [2] Acacia.

digs a small hole at the junction of the paths and buries the blood in the *chaenga*.

TREATMENT FOR MARKED WEAKNESS: when a patient is too weak to get up, the *nganga* prepares a medicine called *mbanda*[1] and adds it to a *chaenga* of boiling water. Leaving the *chaenga* on the fire, he pours enough oil from his calabash to cool the liquid, stirring it all the time. The patient is undressed and the *nganga* ties his animal switch to a broom, dips the end into the *chaenga* and sprinkles the patient's body until there is no more liquid left. Some of the powdered *mbanda* is then taken by mouth in liquid which is added to the patient's porridge.

The next part of the treatment consists of inhalations and hot sponging. For this the *nganga* needs certain roots and leaves which he collects from the bush: *muroro*[2], *mutsambatsi, musingwa*[3], *zumbani* and *nyamaradzo*[4]. After cooking them in a covered pot for two hours, the lid is taken off and the patient inhales the fumes from the herbs. If the patient is too weak to sit up, someone supports him in a sitting position with their arms around his abdomen and a blanket is put over the patient's head while he inhales. When there is no more steam, the patient is laid flat on his reed mat, and his whole body is sponged with leaves out of the pot (the *nganga* waits until they are just cool enough to handle). Before leaving his patient, the *nganga* puts a pot of water containing certain roots[5] beside him and instructs him to drink from the pot whenever he feels thirsty.

In the case of a very sick patient, the *nganga* will sleep the night in the village, not in the patient's hut, because he will be looked after by his relations, but in a separate hut. In the morning he visits the sick man to find out how he spent

[1] Shona name for a root which has been reduced to powder.
[2] Annona senegalensis or stenophylla.   [3] Lannea edulis.
[4] Aspilia brachyphylla
[5] *Chifumuro* (Dicomo anomala), *rambatuku, chipindura* and *dombomakunguo*.

the night. If he is better and strong enough to stretch himself out, the *nganga* makes skin incisions on different parts of his body and rubs powdered medicine into them. The incisions are spaced far apart from each other so that the *nganga* can make fresh ones if he considers the first ineffective. Inhalations and hot sponging are continued morning and evening (but never in the afternoon) until the patient is able to walk.

MOTA: carbuncle. The Mrewa *nganga* follows the special treatment prescribed by the *nganga* of the Mahungwe district[1] who are famous for their success with this scourge. He goes to the patient's village the night before he is to treat him and in the early morning goes into the bush to collect the roots and leaves of *mutova chizimba* and the roots of *mudyanhuka*. He cooks the former in a pot and dries the latter in the sun before grinding them into a powder which he adds to a pot of boiling water. He leaves these two preparations on the fire while he gets hold of a fowl and removes six of its feathers, five of which he ties together in a bundle. The patient is laid flat on the ground, if a man of strong physique he is held down by ropes, otherwise the *nganga* instructs two or three men to hold him while he incises the abscess with a sharp knife. He takes the single feather, thrusts it deep into the incision and cuts another deeper incision in line with the feather. He pours into the cavity the water in which the *mutova chizimba* roots and leaves have been steeping and scoops out the pus with the bunch of feathers. For the next step the *nganga* has to prepare another medicine from the roots of either *musunganyama*[2] or *murumanyama*[3]. After breaking up the roots and boiling them in water, he uses the water to complete the cleansing of the wound. He uses the bunch of feathers as a swab, dipping them into the medicated water and then swabbing the wound until there is no more pus.

[1] In the Inyanga mountains, about 150 miles from Salisbury.
[2] Pteleopsis myrtiflora.   [3] Ostryoderris stuhlmannii.

Finally he takes some soil heaped up by a mole known as a *nhuta*, mixes it in the powdered *mudyanhuka* which he has already prepared and spreads it over the two incisions.

If the carbuncle is very deep-seated the *nganga* uses a different treatment. He cooks *hoshwa* roots with the flesh off a fowl and gives his patient the meat to eat. Care is taken not to throw away the bones which must be kept in a pot filled with clean water. When all the meat has been eaten, the remaining gravy is mixed with the water in which the carcase has been soaked, in the evening the liquid is warmed up and the patient washes his body with it. From then on he adds a little of the medicinal water to his usual washing water until it is finished and the carbuncle has cleared.

CHAPTER 3

Remedies prescribed by the nganga
from Sipolilo

EPILEPSY: This *nganga* classifies the disease into four different types.

1. The first occurs only at the time of the new moon and he attributes it, curiously enough, to the pig. He has, of course, no knowledge of the disorder known in Western medicine as cysticercosis contracted by eating infected pork. His own reason is that a patient suffering from this type of epilepsy moves about and makes noises like a pig when he is in a fit.

To treat it, he breaks up the root of the *murovapasi*, boils it in water, and sponges the patient's body with the water after it has been allowed to cool. He also makes a charm from the roots of two trees[1] which the patient wears round his neck, and from the same roots prepares a liquid medicine which the epileptic takes by mouth.

2. The *nganga* classifies the second type by the characteristic onset of the fit, the subject becoming dizzy and spinning round and round before falling to the ground. He attributes it to the bird *hangaiwa*, a rock pigeon; the fits usually occur in the mid-period of the moon cycle.

To treat it the *nganga* pulverizes the leaves of three trees: the *mbanje mbanje*,[2] the *muchenya* and the *mumbanba*; he fills a reed with the powder and when the epileptic is actually

[1] The *mazizi* and the *chidzunga*.
[2] Cannabis sativa or Tagetes minuta.

169

having a fit, the *nganga* lights the reed and blows the smoke into his patient's face. When the fit is over, the *nganga* sponges him with *mafuta* leaves steeped in water in which roots of the *muzize* tree have been boiled, afterwards he adds some of this liquid to the patient's thin porridge.

3. The third type of epilepsy occurs at no fixed time and is attributed to the activity of a witch. Treatment consists in reducing to powder the roots of the *muringazuva* and *mukondagona* and mixing the powder with the flesh of a *chimupiri* bird. The mixture is taken in liquid porridge three times a day for three months. After he has started this course of medicine, the *nganga* makes incisions on the side of the patient's iliac crests and rubs in ash made from burning a piece of root taken from a tree that crosses a path, mixed with *mhiripiri*[1].

4. The last type is congenital and has the worst prognosis. The *nganga* maintains that epilepsy caused by a pig and a bird are treatable but the epileptic 'who falls into the fire' (the fourth category) cannot be treated. He also holds that any person who has had epilepsy for more than five years cannot be cured.

ASCITES: an abdomen swollen with fluid. This is an extremely common symptom in the African,[2] to treat it the *nganga* soaks the roots of the *mufufu*, the *murutsa* and the *mubarura* trees overnight and in the morning adds the water to the patient's thin porridge. This induces diarrhoea and vomiting and the medicine is administered only once. On the following day the *nganga* starts him on a course of powdered medicine called *mugundamuti*,[3] the powder is stored in a reed and the patient adds a little to his ordinary porridge or relish twice a day for three months.

[1] Chillies.
[2] Because of the great frequency of cirrhosis of the liver.
[3] Made by grinding a piece of root from the tree of the same name with roots of the *nyamazanga*, *mafuriro* and *muroro*.

RUNYOKA RWENHOWA: a disorder characterized by pain and headaches over the anterior fontanelle. The *nganga* crushes the roots of the *murunganyama*, *mutohwa* and *mudzambiringwa* trees, adds the faeces of the *nhimba* (a species of buck known as Grysbok) and soaks the roots in water. The patient drinks the mixture in liquid porridge every morning for a month and a half; at the same time a salve is made from the powdered roots mixed with *mafuta* (castor oil) and it is rubbed over the anterior fontanelle every night for the same period.

The *nganga*, who like his colleague at Mrewa is also a diviner, waits patiently for this treatment to work and only claims his fee after three months; but if at the end of this time the patient has not recovered, he throws his *hakata* to find out which *nganga* his patient should consult next.

SEVERE ABDOMINAL PAIN: is treated by pulverizing six different roots[1] with the bark of the *marorvesa* tree and mixing the fine powder with the dried flesh of any fish and a ground honeycomb. It is stored in an ox's horn which is first cleaned and when all the powder is packed in, the opening is sealed with a piece of animal skin stitched tightly round the top. A hole is pierced in the centre, just large enough to insert either a feather or a small stick from the *mutara* tree; this is left in the hole and three times a day for the next three months the patient sucks some of the sweet mixture from the feather or stick.

MHUKA PUKA: relapsing boils. If a boil starts, discharges, and after an interval another breaks out in a different site, the *nganga* treats the boils with a form of hot fomentation. He boils the root of a small plant, *dumapasi*, with the root of the *dovakari*, adds *mafuta* leaves to the boiling water and

---

[1] *Mukundanyoka*, *muchera wacherera*, *kumwe*, *mugaranjiva*, *mupeto*, and *kafokora*.

applies them over the boil three times a day until the boil clears.

If the condition is a chronic one, he uses a medicine called *hozhwa*, which takes its name from a snail. He grinds the shell into powder, mixes it with the milky sap of the *muhonde*[1] tree and the powdered root of the *musvodzambudzi*, and applies this mixture three times a day to the affected area.

PNEUMONIA: this *nganga*'s treatment is part local and part homeopathic. On the first day of treatment he rubs black ash (made by burning the powdered roots of the chilli plant, *zinyakubaya* and *buvachuru*) into two incisions cut on each side of the outer chest wall. For the medicine (which is taken morning and evening for one month) he boils the roots of the *sukavakadzi*, *mushozhowa* and the *chibayamakono* which oozes a soapy liquid, and adds some of the water in which they have been boiled to the patient's liquid porridge.

NDONGORONGO: a baby's disorder characterized by abdominal pains.[2] The infant is very restless, cries, and the 'veins' on the abdominal wall become visible. The *nganga* crushes three roots—*tsangadzi*[3], *murondo* and *katsvairachuru*— he first soaks them in cold water in which the baby is bathed each day. He then burns the roots and when they are cool gives them to the mother to chew. After she has masticated them she spits the medicine into the child's mouth; the medicated baths and the medicine are given every morning until the child is better.

KUPATIRWA: constipation in infants. The *nganga* reduces to powder the roots of the *mununuwa*[4], *mucherechese*,[5] and *mufufu*[6],

---

[1] Eupho rbiangens.
[2] In older children the complaint is known as *nyongo*.
[3] Stereochlaena cameronii (Chloridion cameronii).
[4] Morotes engleri.   [5] Swartzia madagascariensis.
[6] Securidaca longepedunculata.

passes the powder through a sieve, adds a little water and gives it to the baby to drink. The medicine is usually given only once and it has a quick action, but if it is not effective the baby is given a second dose on the following day. After the bowels have moved, the *nganga* soaks the uncrushed roots of *munguraura* and *moyowatunzi* in water for a day and the baby is given this extract twice a day for a fortnight to prevent it from becoming constipated again.

A simpler treatment is one dose of *mafuta* administered at night.

MAHUMUNYA: mumps. To treat this complaint the *nganga* has to kill a rat, he mixes its flesh with the meat of the *geri* tree and the cast-off skin of any snake. He wraps some of the mixture in a little cloth to make a *zango* and ties it round the patient's neck, the rest of it is smeared on the swellings.

TSIPA: goitre. The remedy consists in crushing the root of a plant similar to the pumpkin, with grain removed from the crop of a fowl. The mixture is then burnt to ashes and the root of the *nyatsinga* tree is mixed in with some salt. The *nganga* cuts tiny incisions over the middle of the goitre, rubs in the medicine and applies his cupping horn. Leaves of the *dovakamwe* are then put in boiling water and applied to the swelling twice a day for four weeks. During this time, usually a fortnight after the first incisions were made, the *nganga* makes further incisions on the lateral sides of the goitre, he rubs some of the powdered ash into them but does not apply the cupping horn.

MHEZI: scabies, very common in infants and children. The *nganga* mixes the fruits of the *nhundurwa*[1], *muvee*, *muchoriondo* and *domboro*, and smears it all over the child's body, it is applied morning and evening for a week.

[1] Solanum incanum.

KUKODOKA: discharging ear. The *nganga* takes a case-bearing caterpillar called *kambuyamuzurure* and crushes it in a cloth with the roots of the *mukonde* and *urimbo*[1] trees. The fluid expressed through the cloth is instilled in the patient's ear each night when he goes to bed, this is done every night for three weeks.

This *nganga* recognizes that deafness can be caused by wax in the ear and uses a lotion to soften and remove it. Oil of the *mupurwa* is mixed with roots and leaves of the *munzviro* tree and the medicine is dropped into the affected ear with a feather.

MHUKA or MUKOTA: bleeding from the nose. The *nganga* prescribes inhalations. He burns the skin of a hippopotamus, the bark of a *muhacha*[2] tree and a porcupine quill. He mixes the ashes with a *mukura* stone (a particular stone found in rivers) which he has previously ground to powder, boiling water is added and the patient inhales the steam. The treatment is repeated twice daily for a month and the *nganga* maintains that it stops the bleeding permanently.

MAZISO or MESO: sore eyes. The *nganga* uses several herbs to cure this condition. He crushes the leaves of the *gwenyanguruve*[3], *tsangadzi* and *mhumhururo*, puts them in a cloth and squeezes hard to force the liquid from the crushed leaves through the cloth and into the patient's eyes. The treatment is continued morning and evening until the eyes are better.

The *nganga* has another eye medicine which he says is particularly effective in cases where the eyes discharge pus. For it he needs a spider's web, which he rolls into a ball and puts in water with bark off the *mubvee* tree[4], leaves of the *mutukutu*[5], fruit of the *chibayamakono* and the root of the *nyazema*. In the morning the patient kneels at the entrance

---

[1] Euphorbia ingens.   [2] Parinari curatellifolia.
[3] Stereochlaena cameronii (Chloridion cameronii).   [4] Kigelia pinnata.
[5] Piliostigma thonningii.

to his hut, opens his eyes with the water and washes his face in it.

KURWARA MWOYO: diseases of the heart. The *nganga* prescribes a medicine called *chipofu* which is made by mixing together the bulbs of various plants[1] and adding them to the patient's mealie porridge. The mixture is taken morning and evening for a month.

KURWARA KWEITSVO: kidney disease, characterized by pain over the renal angles or on the sides of the abdomen. The *nganga* collects the soil scratched up by a fowl when it picks up food, he takes some scratched up by the right claw and some by the left. He then looks for a tree with two branches crossing each other and takes a piece of bark from the point at which they touch. He adds the roots of the *muhwakwa* and *humarabvu* trees and fruit of the *mutara*.[2] All the ingredients are ground into powder and burnt to ash; the *nganga* also reduces the horn of a cattle animal to ash in a *chaenga*. He mixes the two powders, cuts two incisions on each loin and rubs in some of the powder, the remainder is mixed with the mealie porridge which the patient eats every evening for two months.

CHIKANDIWA or CHIPOTSWA: usually attributed to the action of a witch. From the *nganga*'s description it suggests hemiplegia, a paralysis involving one side of the body. He treats it with a medicine called *muhodzakari* made from the surface root of any tree crossing a path, the bark of a tree struck by lightning at the exact point where it was struck, the leaves of a water lily, the water reed and a certain water flower called *kopokora*. The ingredients are ground to powder and the medicine is used in two ways. The *nganga* boils some of the powder, wraps it in a cloth and applies it as a

[1] *Chipofu, moyowechuru* (a plant which grows in the middle of an anthill), *moyowebanana* and *chimaichemichenje.*
[2] Gardenia resiniflua.

175

hot poultice to the affected side. He continues poulticing the patient three times a day for two months, or if the case is a very severe one, for six months. The powder is also prescribed orally and taken in liquid porridge three times a day for six months.

JENDEKUFA: swelling of the scrotal sac and testicles (probably including hydrocele). The *nganga* cuts a small length of root from a tree growing on a river bank, gathers the roots of the *nhindiri*,[1] *chiparurangoma*[2] and *muuyu*, binds them together in a bundle which he soaks in boiling water before gently tapping the swelling with it. This treatment is repeated morning and evening for three months. He also makes incisions on the swelling and rubs in the burnt ashes of the same roots. Apart from these two locally applied remedies, the *nganga* gives the patient a medicine to take in liquid porridge every night until the condition clears.

This *nganga* also treats sterility and barrenness:
NGOMA: the sterile man. This treatment is for a man who is sterile but not impotent. The *nganga* pulverizes the roots of nine[3] trees and divides the powder into two equal parts. One portion is added to the patient's porridge and the other is cooked with the flesh of a cock. The meat is eaten once only, but the porridge is kept and divided in half, one portion is thrown away and the other is eaten twice a day. The treatment is continued for three months. Besides curing the sterility, this treatment is also supposed to make the man capable of having intercourse three times a night, anything less being regarded as abnormal by most Africans.

MUKADZI AKASIRIKWA: the woman who cannot become

[1] Dolchos buchananii.
[1] Borreria dibrachiata.
[3] *Muvukufuka, murovangoma, munguruganga, mujaveni, chinaranaza, chekamasasa, murunganyama* (Pteleopsis myrtifolia), *mutara* (Gardenia resiniflua) and *mukodzombo*.

pregnant. The medicine for this condition is known as *huku chikadzi*. The *nganga* grinds the roots of five trees[1] to powder and cooks it with the flesh of a hen. The woman discards the bones and eats the meat and soup in the morning. Some of the powdered roots, as in the treatment for the sterile man, are kept aside and she adds them to thin porridge which she drinks once a day for four months, unless she falls pregnant before, in which case she will stop taking the medicine. She visits the *nganga* again during the ninth month of her pregnancy and is instructed not to see him again until after she has had the baby.

While I was studying these treatments for specific illnesses prescribed by the Mrewa and Sipolilo *nganga* I found them a curious mixture of common sense, of herbal knowledge (prescribed and administered with the precision of any ordinary medical practitioner), of symbolism, and of prescribed ritual. In describing them here I have not attempted to sort out the magico-religious from the practical or empiric, both elements are so intermingled that it is difficult to know where one stops and the other begins. The *nganga* could not help me because when I questioned them on the reasons for certain treatments they both admitted that treatment of individual cases depended largely on information gained in dreams and on the day to day 'guidance' of their healing *shave*.

---

[1] *Muchecheni* (Ziziphus mauritiana or Oryza sativa), *mutzonzowa* (Carissa edulis), *mutsungu, musukavakadzi* and *musiko*.

Glossary of Shona Terms

ambuya – grandmother

badza – hoe; fee (*badza yako* – your hoe; your fee)

bota – gruel

botso, kutiza – ritual placating of *mudzimu* who died with a grievance

buka – convulsions

bveni – baboon (*shavi rebveni* – baboon spirit)

chaenga – sherd

chibayo – pain in the side

chikandiwa – black magic

chikosoro – cough

chimuti – small piece of wood; divining fee

chipande – charm

chipotswa – black magic

chiremba – title by which *nganga* is addressed

chirume – one of the four faces of wooden divining 'bones'

chitokwadzima – one of the four faces of wooden divining 'bones'

chitsinga – physical disorder believed to be caused by black magic. Medicine for causing such a disorder

chivuno – probably mixture of powdered medicines

danga – enclosure for cattle at night; herd of cattle

dare – meeting place of men of a village

dariro – circle

divisi – charm to cause abundance

fuko – blanket or cloth given to mother-in-law or to appease *mudzimu* of mother-in-law. Burial garment

gakandye – crab

gano – dancing axe

gogodzero – first part of *nganga*'s fee for an emergency call

gono romusha – live beast dedicated to *mudzimu*

gota – hut shared by unmarried male children of family

guru – first stomach of ruminant

hakata – divining bones

Glossary of Shona terms

hangaiwa – rock pigeon

hoka – beer party

hozhwa – snail; snail shell

hwamu – lactescence; meat from inner side of foreleg

imba – dwelling house

jendekufa – hydrocele

kuchenura – to purify ritually

kugamuchira – to receive

kugashira unganga – to receive the powers of divination and healing

kukosora – to cough

kukuya – to grind

kumukika – to feed him by hand

kupumha – to sprinkle

kurova guva – to carry out final funeral ritual (some months after burial)

kuruma – to treat by sucking

kurumika – to cup

kurwara (kweitsvo) – to be unwell (in the kidneys)

kutambira – to receive

kuuchika – to restore fertility

kwami – one of the four faces of the wooden divining 'bones'

lobolo – Nguni word for *roora*, the marriage consideration given by the bride-receiving family to the bride-producing family

madumbu – skirts made from animal skins

mafuta – oil

makomana maviri – name for the result of a casting of the bones which shows two blank faces and exposes the faces called *chitokwadzima* and *nhokwara*

mahumunya – mumps

mangoromera – strength-giving charm

masamba – you have washed (to-day); cattle melons

masangano – one kind of *shave* spirit

mashave – plural form of *shave*

masungiro – ritual offering to parents-in-law on occasion of wife's first pregnancy

matyorwa – meat provided for ritual cleaning required in an extra-marital first pregnancy

mazenda – one kind of *shave* spirit

maziso – eyes

mbamba – cowrie-shell ornament

mbava – thief

mbinjiri – one kind of charm; a small piece of twig threaded on a string

mbiya – porringer

meso – eyes

mhenhu – fee to thank diviner

mhezi – scabies

mhiripiri – chilli

mhondoro – lion; guardian spirit of the tribe; spirit having seniority in heirarchy of spirits

mhuka – sickness of which nose-bleeding is symptom

mombe – one head of cattle

mudzimu – soul of a dead person; spirit elder

mugoti – stirring stick used in cooking

muhacha – cork tree; parinari caratellaefolia; tree most commonly associated with ritual

munda – land in which a family cultivates its food crops

munyai – representative, esp. of suitor in marriage negotiations

mupfuhwira – love potion

mupurwa – leguaan (large lizard)

muriwo (wenyemba) – leaves (of cow pea) cooked as spinach

muroyi – witch; wizard; person with anti-social habits

murumiko – cupping horn

murungu – European

musha – village; home

musharo – doctor's fee

mushonga – medicine

musika – whisk, used in cooking

musiya – blood from slaughtered animal

musumo – small pot of beer whose presentation indicates that the preparation of beer has been completed

mutakati – Zulu word meaning witch or wizard

mutatu – a *hakata* throw which suggests agreement with the previous throw

muteyo – poison ordeal

muvuki – diviner who uses no external apparatus

mweredzo – beer drink distinct from, but ritually connected with, either sacrifice of a beast or burial of a person

mwoyo – heart

ndarira – copper or brass wire; bangle

ndebvu – beard

ndyukura – special headress worn by *nganga*

Glossary of Shona terms

nganga – Shona doctor; diviner; healer. Note that the first 'ng' is pronounced as the 'ng' is pronounced in singer

ngozi – aggrieved spirit

ngundu – head-dress

ngwena – crocodile

nhanga – hut in which the girls of a village sleep

nhekwe – snuff box

nhetemedzi – electric catfish

nhimba – grysbok

nhindiri – wild lupin

nhokwara – one of the four faces of wooden divining 'bones'

nhundurwa – bitter apple

nhuta – mole rat; festering sore

nyamukuta – midwife

nyengeredzi – sea shell

nyongo – intestinal parasite; flatulence

nyora – tattoo mark; incisions made on patient's skin by *nganga*

nzungu – ground nut

ropa – blood

rukuva – pot shelf inside the main hut, at which prayers are addressed to spirit elders

rukwa – protective charm against theft

rukweza – finger millet; Eleusine coracana

runyoka – veneral disease

rushanga – sacred enclosure

rusumuro – preliminary fee for summoning *nganga*; it might take the form of a bracelet; derives from the transitive verb meaning to raise

sabuku – village headman

sadza – stiff porridge

sekuru – grandfather; uncle

shano – diviner's fee

shato – python

shave (*shavi*) – alien patronal spirit

showera – stye in the eye

takutuka chiremba – 'We have scolded you, doctor'

tsambo – bracelet

tsipa – goitre

tsito – charcoal

tsomo – dancing axe

urindi – sickness of the lungs

Glossary of Shona terms

uroyi – witchcraft

vadzimu – plural form of *mudzimu*

varoyi – plural form of *muroyi*

vatete – paternal aunt

wizi – shell-like ornament worn on chest of some *nganga*; synonym *ndoro*

zango – cloth-wrapped charm

zaru – a *hakata* throw suggesting disagreement with a previous one

zuva – sun; day; delayed closing of the fontanelle

Index

Index

divination, 63-4; of lost or stolen articles, 54-5; powers of, 27-8; of *shave's* selection of host, 39-40, 41; without *hakata*, 123, 128, 131

diviner: consultation with, 86-90; fee, 87, 88, 89, 90; and spirit possession, 79-85; use of *hakata*, 63, 75-9

divisi medicine, 71-2

divisi rakaipa (bad *divisi*), 71-2

divisi rakanaka (good *divisi*), 71

dombonakunguo roots, 166n

domboro tree, 173

dovakamwe tree, 158n, 173

dovakari root, 171

dreams, of cures and medicines, 123, 125, 127, 129, 131, 132

dress, of mediums, 80

dumapasi root, 171

Dzivaguru (a rain-maker), 26

ear, discharging, 174

eating habits, 21

eating place, 18

Edwards, W., 61, 76

elders, village, 19

emotional contingencies, remedies against, 54, 69-70, 72-3

epidemics, protection from, 92-3

epilepsy, 91, 92, 136, 169-70

equipment, of *nganga*, 59

ethics, professional, 116-18

etiquette, 19-22

European medicine, attitude to, 114-19

European *shave*, 41

Europeans, never accused of witchcraft, 52

Evans-Pritchard, Professor E., 29-30, 117n

excreta, use in cures and spells, 28, 29, 67

exorcism, 67-9

eyes, sore, 174

family, respect for parents, 33

family life, 17-18, 20, 21-2, 33

family unit, 17

feeding methods, 162n

fees, 87, 88, 89, 90, 91, 93, 105; for medicines, 67; training, 58, 59-60

Field, M. J., 30, 44, 46, 47, 83-4, 85

fireplace, 17

fontanelle, closure of, 104, 108-9, 110

food, 18

fuko (shroud, also diviner's fee), 90, 96n, 135, 137

Ga people, 30, 44, 46, 47, 83

gakandye (crab), 165

gano (axe), 59, 80

gardens, 18

gariro root, 108n

gastric complaint, 140

genital swelling, 176

geri tree, 173

gifts: giving and receiving of, 21-2; prayer of thanks for, 36

Gluckman, M., 45n

go-between, 22

goat sacrifice, 64, 137

gogodzero (diviner's fee), 89, 90

goitre, 173

gomorara (mistletoe), 163

gono romusha ceremony, 135n

gota (boys' hut), 17

granaries, 18

grandfather's spirit: and illness, 135, 138, 140, 142-3; propitiation of, 94-9, 130, 131, 135-6, 137, 138-40, 141, 142-3

grandmother's spirit, and illness, 135, 137, 139, 141, 142, 143

grandparents, 17; respect for, 33, 37; spirits of, 34-5, 37, 78, 127, 129, 130-2

graves, visited by witches, 44, 47

greeting customs, 20-1

guardian spirits, 32-8

guilt complex, of self-confessed witches, 47

gunpowder, as bad medicine, 73

Index

guru (small intestine), 98
gwendere roots, 161
gwenyanguruve tree, 174

hakata (divining bones), 57, 63, 75-9
hangaiwa (rock pigeon), 169
headaches, 127
headman, 19
heart diseases, 175
heat treatment, 158
hemiplegia, 175-6
herbal remedies, 65-74, 155-77; dreams about, 128, 129, 131, 132; preparation of, 155-9
herbalists: attempt to form association, 117; consultation with, 86, 90-3; fee, 91, 93; and treatment of symptoms, 63
hoka (beer party), 18n
hoshwa roots, 168
hozhwa medicine, 172
huku chikadzi medicine, 177
humarabvu tree, 175
huts, 17-18
hyenas, ridden by witches, 44
hygiene, 29n
hypnosis, state of possession as, 83-4

imba (main hut), 17
incest, to protect crops, 72
incisions, 156
'indirect approach', 22
inhalations, 66, 158-9
inheritance: of spirit, 41; of witch's evil by daughter, 43, 44
insufflations, powder for, 157

Javaneka (a *nganga*), 128-9
jekamasasa tree, 71n
jendekufa (genital swelling), 176
jeneko (last pot of beer), 61
Jexa (a *nganga*), 128
Joel (a *nganga*), 129-31
justice, 19

kafokora root, 171n
Kandeya reserve, 126
kapande (organizer of trial by ordeal), 49
kariringwe tree, 160
karomo (divining throw), 78
katsai roots, 164
katsvairachuru roots, 172
kidney diseases, 175
kopokora flower, 175
kuchenjedza murwere (gift to herbalist), 91
kuchenura (divining), 87
kufara ceremony, 77
kugamuchira (receiving), 22n
kugashira nganga ceremony, 60-1
kukodoka (discharging ear), 174
kukosora (persistent cough), 161-2
kukuya process, 155n
kumukika neminwe (feeding method), 162n
kumwe root, 171n
kupatirwa (constipation), 172-3
kupindura medicine, 71
kupumha (sucking out), 124n
kupwera illness, 111
kurova guva ceremony, 137
kurwadza kweitsvo (kidney disease), 175
kurwara kwemusana kwokuruyiwa (backache), 165
kurwara nemoyo (heart diseases), 175
Kutamba mudzimu (bull sacrifice), 94n
kutambira (receiving), 22n
kutangira illness, 111
kutiza botso ceremony, 36
kuuchika tree, 71
kwami (divining bone), 75-6
kwamu (sacrificial meat), 97

lark droppings, medicine from, 67
leaves, as medicine, 66, 158
leprosy, 91
lion, tribal spirit's possession of, 130n
liquid medicines, 157-8

Index

Index

Index

Index

rain-making, 26
rambatuku roots, 166*n*
Razi (a *nganga*), 125-6
religious ritual, 19, 30, 31, 34, 35, 36, 38, 88, 137
restraining influence, of guardian spirits, 37
rivalry, professional, 117
river bed, qualifying by living in, 61-2
roots, crushed, 155-6; in naming ritual, 105; in preventive medicine, 109
roots, dried, 66
roots, soaked, 107-8
ropa mudodi (blood in stools), 160
rukuva (cooking-pot shelf), 37
rukwa medicine, 47, 54, 72
rukweza meal, 160
runyoka medicine (to protect marriage), 54, 72-3
runyoka rwenhowa illness, 171
rushanga (shrine), 96
rusumuro (bangle), 91*n*

sabuku (headman), 19
sadza (porridge), 18, 156
scabies, 173
scapegoat, witch as, 51
scarification, 68-9
Seke reserve, 139
sekuru (divining throw), 78*n*
sekuru (grandfather's spirit), 34
Sena mashave, 79, 80
sex-determination: medicines for, 71; *nganga*'s ability in, 54
shaman, 132-3; difference from *nganga*, 132
shano (herbalist's fee), 91*n*
shato (snake), 70
shave (alien spirit), 39-41, 56, 58; as cause of illness, 143; divination of, 78, 79, 88; as patronal spirit, 41, 57; possession by, 79-81, 127-9, 130-1
shells, as charm against witchcraft, 110

Sipolilo, remedies of herbalist from, 155, 169-77
skin complaints, 66
skin incisions, 156-7
skins, animal, in medicines, 70
sorcerers, 29, 45-6
sore throat, 135-6
specialist diviner, 89-90
spells, casting of, 28-9
spirits, belief in sickness caused by, 24-5, 32, 135, 136, 137-9, 140, 141, 142-3. *See also* aggrieved spirits, alien spirits, etc.
spiritual endowment: belief in, 27, 28, 30, 131-2; proof of, 56-8
spiritualist, *nganga* as, 27, 28-9, 31
sterility, 46, 100, 176
stramonium, 67
strangers, fear of, 52, 68
strength, instilled by medicine, 70, 74, 111
subconscious, role of, 132
sucking-out treatment, 124, 134
suffering, and *nganga*'s initiation, 133
sukavakadzi roots, 172
supernatural, anything unusual attributed to, 40-1, 144
symbolism, 25
sympathetic magic, 25, 73, 107, 110

taboos, 63-4, 101
talents, bestowed by *shave*, 39, 41
Tambadzai (a *nganga*), 124-5
theft: belief in *nganga*'s detective powers as deterrent to, 54; of crops, 72
thief, medicine to help, 72
totems, 64*n*
Tracey, H., 76
tradition, respect for, 37
training, 58-9, 61-3
trance, and spirit possession, 27, 82
transference, 67-8
trial by ordeal, 46-7, 49-50